Sabrina Richards Sopranzi

FLASH on
English for
MECHANICS &
ELECTRONICS

ESP
Series

Contents

🎧 1 MP3 audio files downloadable from www.elionline.com

1 Materials

A mechanical engineer uses different materials to build **machinery** or **tools**. A specific knowledge of materials is required, concerning qualities, properties, costs and general characteristics.

1 **What are these objects made of? Match the words in the box with the pictures, then read the text.**

| steel | gold | wood | plastic |
| glass | ceramic | | |

1 _____

2 _____

3 _____

4 _____

5 _____

6 _____

When a machine or a tool is made, the most suitable material must be chosen by considering its properties, which can be classified as mechanical, thermal, electrical and chemical. The main types of materials used in mechanical engineering are metals, polymer materials, ceramics and composite materials.

The most commonly used materials are metals, which can be divided into ferrous and non-ferrous. They can be used in their pure form or mixed with other elements. In this second case we have an **alloy** and it is used to **improve** some properties of the metals. The most commonly used ferrous metals are iron and alloys which use iron. Because iron is soft and pasty it is not suitable to be used as a structural material, so a small amount of **carbon** is added to it to make **steel** alloy.

Non-ferrous metals contain little or no iron. The most common non-ferrous metals used in mechanics are **copper**, **zinc**, **tin** and **aluminium**. Some common non-ferrous alloys are **brass** (formed by mixing copper and zinc), **bronze** (formed by mixing copper and tin) and other aluminium alloys which are used in the aircraft industry. Other examples of materials used in mechanical engineering are **plastic** and **rubber**.

PVC or polyvinyl chloride is a type of plastic and is used to **insulate wires** and **cables**. Rubber is a polymer and its best property is elasticity, as it returns to its original size and shape after deformation. Ceramic materials are good insulators: hard, resistant and strong, but **brittle**. Composite materials are made up of two or more materials combined to improve their mechanical properties. **Concrete** is reinforced with steel and is used in building engineering.

2 **Read the text again and match the words with their definitions.**

1 alloy
2 steel
3 PVC
4 concrete
5 brass
6 ferrous materials
7 ceramic
8 iron

a ☐ a type of plastic used for insulation
b ☐ a combination of different metals
c ☐ an alloy formed by mixing iron and carbon
d ☐ an alloy formed by mixing copper and zinc
e ☐ metals containing iron
f ☐ a composite material used to build houses
g ☐ a metal not suitable as structural material
h ☐ a good insulator but brittle

3 **Read the text again and answer the questions.**

1 What is the basic classification of metals?
2 What are the characteristics of iron?
3 Why are alloys created?
4 Which materials are good insulators?
5 Is steel an alloy? Which metal does it contain?

4 🎧 1 **Listen and complete the definitions with the words in the box.**

> cooking   coins   alloy   air   copper   wires   steel
> carbon   gold   ~~ferrum~~   expensive   ductile

Iron: Its Latin name is (1) *ferrum*. It is magnetic and has a silvery colour. In prehistoric times it was used to make ornaments and weapons. If exposed to the (2) _____, it **oxidises**.

(3) _____: It is one of the most widely used metals by humans. In prehistoric times it was used to make cooking utensils, (4) _____ and ornamental objects. It is used in (5) _____ and cables.

(6) _____: It is the most (7) _____ metal and is used to create precious jewellery. It is the most (8) _____ metal.

(9) _____: It is an (10) _____ formed from iron and (11) _____. It can contain between 2.1% and 4% carbon. It is also used for (12) _____ utensils and pans.

5 **Complete the following diagram.**

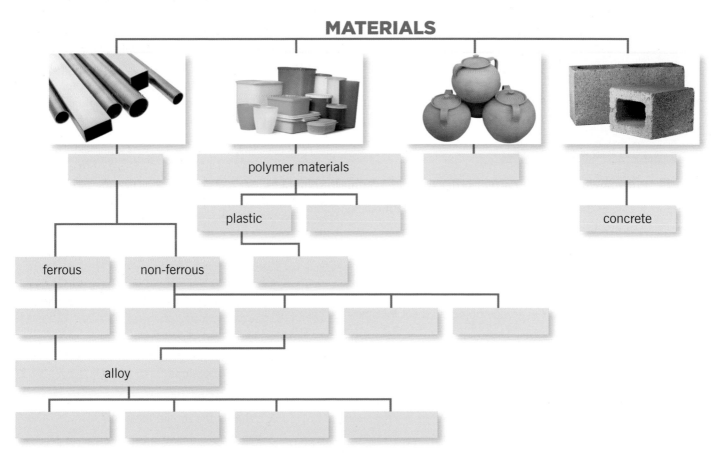

MATERIALS

| | polymer materials | | concrete |

plastic

ferrous   non-ferrous

alloy

6 Writing **Write a summary of the texts in exercises 1 and 4 following the flow chart.**

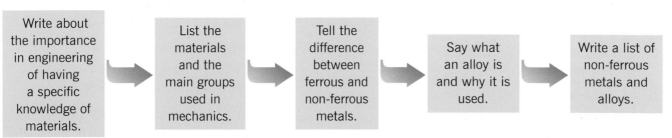

Write about the importance in engineering of having a specific knowledge of materials. → List the materials and the main groups used in mechanics. → Tell the difference between ferrous and non-ferrous metals. → Say what an alloy is and why it is used. → Write a list of non-ferrous metals and alloys.

Metal processes

7 🎧 2 **Listen and complete the texts about the different processes metals can go through.**

Casting is a 6,000 year old process. It is the oldest and most well-known technique based on three fundamental steps: moulding, melting and (1) _____. First the pattern is made to form the **mould**. Then an empty mould is created, and finally the empty cavity is filled with molten metal which is then left to solidify into the shape. Casting materials are usually (2) _____ but can also be plastic, resin or various cold materials for example (3) _____. Casting is usually used for making complex shapes.

Drawing is a manufacturing process for producing wires, **bars** and (4) _____ by pulling on material through a series of **dies** until it increases in length. It is divided into two types: sheet metal drawing, and wire, (5) _____, and **tube** drawing. Drawing is usually done at room temperature but it can be performed at elevated temperatures to hot work large wires, **rods** or **hollow** sections in order to reduce forces.

Forging is the process by which metal is heated and shaped by a compressive force using a **hammer** or a press. It is used to produce large quantities of identical parts, such as (6) _____ parts in the automobile industry. Cold forging is done at a low temperature using (7) _____ metals and plastic. Hot forging is done at a high temperature and makes metal easier to shape without breaking. In the past, forging was done by a **blacksmith** using a hammer. Nowadays industrial forging is done with (8) _____ powered by a machine.

8 **Put the words in the correct order to make complete sentences.**

1 taking their forms / fluid substances / into moulds / solidify _____

2 drawing / room temperature / is done at _____

3 not essential / heat / is / in the drawing process _____

4 in the past / using / forging / a hammer / was done _____

5 can be / brittle materials / extrusion / done / with _____

6 many / is used / everyday objects / sheet forming / to make _____

9 **Pairwork Read the texts again and write the correct processes that produce the objects listed below.**

Product	Process
1 wires	_____
2 pasta	_____
3 sheet	_____
4 bricks	_____
5 tubes	_____
6 rods and bars	_____
7 golden leaves	_____
8 machine parts	_____
9 concrete	_____

10 **Read the texts again and answer the following questions.**

1 Which steps are included in casting?

2 What is the mould used for?

3 What does drawing use in order to process metals?

4 What types of drawing are there?

5 What kind of process is forging?

6 How was forging done in the past?

7 What does rolling consist of?

8 What materials can be used in rolling?

9 What are the advantages of extrusion?

10 What materials can be used in extrusion?

11 What kind of process is sheet metal forming?

12 What can vary in sheet metal forming?

Rolling is a metal forming (9) _____ in which a material (metal, plastic, paper or glass) is passed through a pair of rollers. According to the (10) _____ of material rolled, there is hot rolling or cold rolling.

Extrusion is a process used to produce objects with a fixed cross-sectional profile. A material is pushed or drawn through a die of the desired cross-section. The two main (11) _____ of this process are its ability to create very complex cross-sections and work materials that are brittle. The extrusion process can be done with hot or cold materials. Commonly extruded materials include metals, polymers, (12) _____, concrete and foodstuffs.

Ceramic can also be formed into shapes via extrusion. Terracotta extrusion is used to produce **pipes**. Many modern **bricks** are also manufactured using a brick extrusion process. Extrusion is also used in (13) _____ processing. Products such as certain pastas, many breakfast cereals, French fries, dry pet food and ready-to-eat snacks are mostly manufactured by extrusion.

Sheet metal forming is simply metal formed into thin and **flat** pieces. The basic forms can be cut and **bent** into a variety of different shapes. Everyday objects are constructed with this process. There are many different metals that can be made into sheet metal, such as aluminium, (14) _____, copper, steel, tin, nickel and titanium. For decorative uses, important sheet metals include silver, gold, and platinum. Sheet metal forming is used in car bodies, airplane wings and roofs for (15) _____.

MY GLOSSARY

alloy /ˈælɔɪ/ _____

aluminium /æljʊˈmɪniəm/ _____

bar /bɑː(r)/ _____

bent /bent/ _____

blacksmith /ˈblæksmɪθ/ _____

brass /brɑːs/ _____

brick /brɪk/ _____

brittle /ˈbrɪtl̩/ _____

bronze /brɒːnz/ _____

cable /ˈkeɪbl̩/ _____

carbon /ˈkɑːbn̩/ _____

casting /ˈkɑːstɪŋ/ _____

concrete /ˈkɒŋkriːt/ _____

copper /ˈkɒpə(r)/ _____

die /daɪ/ _____

drawing /ˈdrɔːɪŋ/ _____

extrusion /ɪkˈstruːʒn/ _____

flat /flæt/ _____

hammer /ˈhæmə(r)/ _____

hollow /ˈhɒləʊ/ _____

to improve /tuː ɪmˈpruːv/ _____

to insulate /tuː ˈɪnsjʊleɪt/ _____

machinery /məˈʃiːnəri/ _____

mould /məʊld/ _____

to oxidise /tuː ˈɒksɪdaɪz/ _____

pipe /paɪp/ _____

plastic /ˈplæstɪk/ _____

rod /rɒd/ _____

rolling /ˈrəʊlɪŋ/ _____

rubber /ˈrʌbə(r)/ _____

shape /ʃeɪp/ _____

sheet /ʃiːt/ _____

steel /stiːl/ _____

tin /tɪn/ _____

tool /tuːl/ _____

tube /tjuːb/ _____

wire /waɪə(r)/ _____

zinc /zɪŋk/ _____

2 Properties of materials

According to the reaction of some material to the appliance of a force, there are different materials properties which are included in the following categories: **mechanical**, **thermal**, **electrical-magnetic**, **chemical**.

Mechanical properties

Strength The most common mechanical property is strength, or the ability of a material to resist forces without breaking, bending, shattering or changing in any permanent way. For example: if elastic material is stretched, the change will be temporary; but it will be permanent with plastic or metal materials.

When a force is applied to a material, as when a weight is put on the end of a rope, certain forces inside the rope cause it to stretch. In mechanics, the weight that is applied is called the *load*. The force within the rope that causes it to stretch is called the *stress*. The actual change, in this case the stretching, is called the *strain*.

A material can undergo three changes due to stress. It can stretch, it can get shorter, or it may divide into layers. The stress that causes a material to stretch is called *tensile* stress. The stress that causes a material to get shorter is called *compressive* stress, while the stress that causes a material to divide into layers is called *shearing* stress.

STRENGTH OF MATERIALS (in pounds per square inch)			
Material	**Tensile**	**Compressive**	**Shearing**
Aluminium	58,000	35,000	35,000
Brick		1,500 – 3,000	
Bronze	85,000		
Cast iron	60,000	145,000	70,000
Concrete		2,000	
Copper	50,000 – 70,000		
Stone		8,000	
Wrought iron	48,000	25,000	38,000

Plasticity This is the ability of a material to be permanently changed in shape. For example, the plasticity of molten aluminium can be demonstrated by pouring it into a mould. Once the aluminium has cooled down, it can be removed from the mould and has a new shape. *Malleability*, which occurs when metals are hammered or rolled into thin sheets, is also a property associated with plasticity. Gold, for example, is one of the most malleable metals. Other common metals in order of malleability are silver, copper, aluminium, tin, zinc, and lead.
Ductility, which is the ability of certain solid substances to undergo permanent changes in shape without breaking usually by stretching the length is another property. For example, a piece of copper can be stretched to make a thin wire, but the shape of a brick cannot be permanently changed except by breaking it. Ductility is a valuable property of many metals including aluminium, gold, iron, nickel, and silver.
The term *malleability* is often used in place of *ductility* when describing the property of metals that allows them to be hammered into thin sheets.

Elasticity This is the ability of a substance to return to its original shape or volume after it has been changed by a force. All substances have some elasticity. Some familiar uses of elasticity are the springs in vehicles and the rubber and air in balls.

Hardness This is the resistance of a material to surface abrasion, scratching and indentation. The standard scale of hardness is as follows: soapstone, gypsum, chalk, fluorite, apatite, porcelain, quartz, topaz, corundum, diamond.

Brittleness This is the property of a material that is hard but easily broken.

Fatigue This is the ability to resist repeated stress cycles and tension.

1 Read the text and decide if the statements are true (T) or false (F).

1 The ability of a material to resist forces is the most common mechanical property. _____
2 Strain means the weight applied to a material. _____
3 A material doesn't undergo any changes when under stress. _____
4 Shearing is the stress that divides materials into layers. _____
5 Aluminium is less tensile than bronze, but more than brick. _____
6 Cast iron is as compressive as concrete. _____
7 The ability of metals to be hammered or rolled into thin sheets is called plasticity. _____
8 Diamond is the hardest and chalk is the softest. _____

2 Match the words with their definitions.

1 brittleness
2 strain
3 plasticity
4 hardness

a ☐ the state of a material which is distorted by forces acting on it
b ☐ resistance to cutting, indentation, abrasion
c ☐ the tendency to fracture without appreciable deformation and under low stress
d ☐ a property of certain materials by which deformation due to a stress is largely retained after removal of the stress

Thermal properties

Thermal properties describe how a material behaves when its temperature changes.
Thermal conductivity, thermal expansion and melting point are among the main thermal properties.

Thermal conductivity In physics, thermal conductivity is the ability of a material to conduct heat. Metals in general have high thermal conductivity, as they are able to transmit heat energy. Thermal conductivity is important in materials science, research, electronics, building insulation and related fields, especially when high operating temperatures are achieved.
Cooling solutions for electronics or turbines usually use high-thermal conductivity materials such as copper, aluminium, and silver to cool down specific elements. However, applications in buildings or furnaces use low thermal conductive materials such as polystyrene and alumina for insulation purposes.

Thermal expansion This is the change in dimensions that occurs with most materials as the temperature is increased or decreased.
Heat causes expansion because it increases the vibrations of atoms or molecules in a material. Different materials expand by different amounts when the temperature is raised by one degree. For example: aluminium expands twice as much as iron under the same temperature increase.

Melting point The temperature at which a material turns suddenly from solid to liquid. For metals the maximum operating temperature is usually around two thirds of the melting temperature.

3 **Read the text and answer the questions.**

1 What is the property of thermal conductivity?
2 Which materials are more able to transmit heat energy?
3 What is meant by thermal expansion?

4 Do all materials expand in the same way?
5 What happens when the temperature reaches melting point?

4 **Pairwork** **Take turns with your partner at asking and answering questions about thermal properties.**

- What is heat energy?
- How is energy transferred?

- Which are main conductors of energy?

Electrical-magnetic and chemical properties

Electrical conductivity This is the ability of a material to conduct electrical charge. All materials conduct electricity, but some materials such as rubber and glass allow so few electrons to get through that the current is hardly noticeable. These materials are called *insulators*. Other materials, such as metals, conduct current readily. These materials are called *conductors*. Metal, in general, is the best conductor, and silver, copper, gold, and aluminium are among the best metallic conductors.

Electrical resistivity This is the ability of a material to resist, or oppose, the transport of electrical charge in response to an external electrical field.

A **chemical property** is any of the properties of a material that become evident during a chemical reaction. Chemical properties can be useful to identify an unknown substance or to purify it or separate it from other substances.

Resistance to chemicals This is the ability of a material to resist chemical attack and to withstand corrosion processes such as oxidation.

Atomic volume This is the volume occupied by a gram-atom of an element in the solid state.

Density This is the mass of material per unit volume (kg/m^3).

5 **Read the text and find the following information.**
- Difference between insulators and conductors.
- Best electrical conductors.
- Properties useful to identify unknown substances.
- One of the chemical properties.

6 **Complete the text about insulators and conductors with the words from the box.**

heat	wire	conductors	insulators	thermal	material	hot	dangerous	electricity	copper

Some materials let heat pass or flow through easily and these are called (**1**) _____ conductors. Other materials don't let (**2**) _____ pass or flow through them and these are called thermal insulators. Among the best (**3**) _____ arc carbon and most metals (especially silver and copper). Think about metal saucepans; they allow the heat from the cooker to pass through easily to heat up the water and food inside them. The best (**4**) _____ include wood, cork, concrete, plastic and fabrics such as thermal vests and oven gloves. If a (**5**) _____ is a good insulator then it's a poor conductor. Heat only moves from (**6**) _____ things to colder things. As well as conducting or insulating against heat, materials can also conduct or insulate against (**7**) _____. As a general rule, materials that conduct heat well are also good conductors of electricity (e.g. metals such as copper, iron, steel and aluminium). Wood, plastic, glass and rubber are both thermal and electrical insulators. These are very important and have really essential uses. For example, (**8**) _____ wires allow electricity to flow through them, but each (**9**) _____ is covered in plastic and all are encased in plastic tubing so electricity won't flow out and give you a shock; it's insulated. Remember, electricity can be (**10**) _____. It can even be conducted through the sweat on your body!

7 **Pairwork** **Take turns with your partner at asking and answering questions about electrical and magnetic properties.**

MY GLOSSARY

brittleness /ˈbrɪt(ə)lnəs/ _____
conductivity /kɒndʌkˈtɪvɪti/ _____
density /ˈdɛnsɪti/ _____
ductility /dʌkˈtɪlɪti/ _____
elasticity /elaˈstɪsɪti/ _____
expansion /ɪkˈspanʃ(ə)n/ _____
fatigue /fəˈtiːg/ _____
hardness /ˈhɑːdnəs/ _____
layer /ˈleɪə/ _____

malleability /malɪəˈbɪlɪti/ _____
plasticity /plaˈstɪsɪti/ _____
resistivity /ˌrɪzɪˈstɪvɪti/ _____
to melt /tə mɛlt/ _____
to shear /tə ʃɪə/ _____
to shutter /tə ˈʃatə/ _____
to strain /tə streɪn/ _____
to stretch /tə strɛtʃ/ _____

3 Technical drawing

1 **Read the text about technical drawing and label the pictures.**

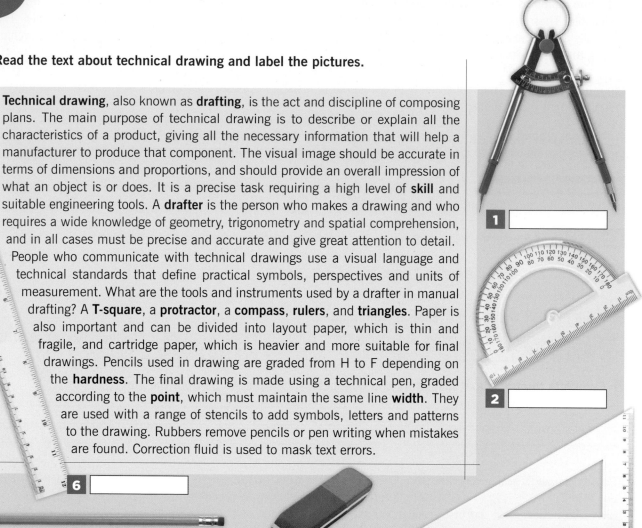

Technical drawing, also known as **drafting**, is the act and discipline of composing plans. The main purpose of technical drawing is to describe or explain all the characteristics of a product, giving all the necessary information that will help a manufacturer to produce that component. The visual image should be accurate in terms of dimensions and proportions, and should provide an overall impression of what an object is or does. It is a precise task requiring a high level of **skill** and suitable engineering tools. A **drafter** is the person who makes a drawing and who requires a wide knowledge of geometry, trigonometry and spatial comprehension, and in all cases must be precise and accurate and give great attention to detail. People who communicate with technical drawings use a visual language and technical standards that define practical symbols, perspectives and units of measurement. What are the tools and instruments used by a drafter in manual drafting? A **T-square**, a **protractor**, a **compass**, **rulers**, and **triangles**. Paper is also important and can be divided into layout paper, which is thin and fragile, and cartridge paper, which is heavier and more suitable for final drawings. Pencils used in drawing are graded from H to F depending on the **hardness**. The final drawing is made using a technical pen, graded according to the **point**, which must maintain the same line **width**. They are used with a range of stencils to add symbols, letters and patterns to the drawing. Rubbers remove pencils or pen writing when mistakes are found. Correction fluid is used to mask text errors.

1 ☐
2 ☐
3 ☐
4 ☐
5 ☐
6 ☐

2 **Read the text again and choose the correct answer.**

1 Technical drawing is needed to...
   A make a scale of the product.
   B practise pens, rulers and stencils.
   C let the manufacturer understand the requirements.

2 The drafter needs...
   A some paper and a pencil.
   B a wide range of technical instruments.
   C the final product.

3 Paper is chosen considering...
   A what sort of drawing the drafter is going to make.
   B the pencils he/she is going to use.
   C the drafter's preference.

4 Pencils are graded according to...
   A hardness.
   B hardness and colour.
   C hardness and point.

5 A technical pen...
   A makes regular lines.
   B maintains the same line width.
   C draws lines of the same length.

6 When mistakes are found...
   A we can't correct them.
   B they're removed with correction fluid.
   C stencil can cover them.

3 🎧 3 **Listen and complete the text with the words in the box.**

> creation   advantages   boards   drawings   software   defects   faster
> instructions   traditional   reduce   modification   electronically

CAD/CAM systems

Drawing (1) _____ and manual drawing are not always precise and rapid: (2) _____ design is usually slow, especially in its revision and (3) _____. For this reason manufacturing firms have **replaced** manual drawing with computer-aided design (CAD) to **carry out** functions related to design and production. This computer technology assists the designer in the (4) _____, modification and analysis of a physical object. Nowadays computer (5) _____ can easily provide a three-dimensional drawing, which allows engineering designers to see how mechanical components may **fit** together without making models thus **saving** a lot of time. CAD is much (6) _____ and more accurate than manual drawing; designs can be quickly modified, reproduced and transmitted (7) _____. Computer simulated analysis of the model helps experts find problems and (8) _____ without building prototypes, in this way saving a lot of money and time. When the design is ready, the CAD system can generate the detailed (9) _____ needed to start product manufacturing. When CAD systems are linked to manufacturing equipment controlled by computers, they form an integrated CAD/CAM system. Computer-aided manufacturing (CAM) offers significant (10) _____ over traditional approaches by controlling manufacturing equipment with computers instead of human labour. CAM converts the design of a component into computer language and it gives (11) _____ to the computer regarding machine operations.

Thanks to CAD/CAM systems it is possible to eliminate operator errors and (12) _____ manufacturing costs.

4 **Read the text again and match each sentence with its ending.**

1 CAD helps designers
2 By using a CAD technology
3 Unlike manual drawing, CAD
4 CAD allows us to save
5 CAD designs can be
6 CAM is the use of computer software
7 The CAM system turns
8 CAD/CAM systems

a ☐ seen from any angle and are easily manipulated.
b ☐ to draw, modify and correct designs.
c ☐ the design into computer language.
d ☐ defects can be easily found.
e ☐ provides three-dimensional drawings.
f ☐ time and money.
g ☐ minimise errors and manufacturing costs.
h ☐ to control machine tools in the manufacturing process.

MY GLOSSARY

to carry out /tə ˈkæri aʊt/ _____
drafter /drɑːftə(r)/ _____
drafting /drɑːftɪŋ/ _____
to fit /tə fɪt/ _____
hardness /hɑːdnes/ _____
point /pɔɪnt/ _____
prototype /prəʊtətaɪp/ _____
protractor /prəˈtræktə(r)/ _____

to replace /tə rɪˈpleɪs/ _____
ruler /ˈruːlə(r)/ _____
skill /skɪl/ _____
technical drawing /teknɪkl ˈdrɔːɪŋ/ _____
to save /tə seɪv/ _____
triangle /traɪæŋgl/ _____
T-square /tiːskweə(r)/ _____
width /wɪdθ/ _____

4 | Machine tools

A **machine tool** uses a power source to modify the shape of metal components of machines. It is a sort of machine used as a tool in the making of other machines. Machine tools were powered in the Middle Ages by humans and animals, and later by the energy captured by **waterwheels**. After the Industrial Revolution, most machine tools were powered by **steam engine** and nowadays by electricity.

Machine tools can be operated manually, or under automatic control. In the 1960s, computers gave more flexibility to the process. Such machines became known as computerized numerical control (CNC) machines. They could precisely repeat sequences, and could produce much more complex pieces than even the most **skilled** tool operators.

Let's examine the main **features** of some of the most commonly used machine tools.

Turning machine
The engine **lathe** is the most important of all the machine tools. It is used to produce external or internal cylindrical surfaces. The piece is held by the machine and is rotated while a cutting tool removes excess metal from the external diameter. Internal turning consists of enlarging and finishing a **hole**.

Shaper
This is a metal-cutting machine used to produce or modify flat surfaces. The cutting tool moves cutting on the forward **stroke**, with the piece feeding automatically towards the tool during each return stroke. Shapers can be horizontal or vertical.

Drilling machine
It is used to produce circular holes in metal with a twist drill. It also uses a variety of other cutting tools to perform the basic hole-machining operations.

1 Read the texts about metalworking processes and complete the table.

Machine tool	Final result	Description
turning machine	external and internal flat surface	It removes excess metal from the external diameter. It enlarges and finishes a hole.
	specific shape	It cuts flat metal surfaces.
	holes	It uses a twist drill to make holes.
	flat surface	It cuts the piece.
	specific shape	It changes the shape of a workpiece.
	cut pieces	It cuts various parts using a continuous band of metal with teeth.
	finishing	It removes excessive material from parts.

2 Read the texts again and decide if the following sentences are true (T) or false (F).

1 Turning machines remove excess metal from the external diameter and enlarge and finish a hole. ____
2 Shapers can only be vertical. ____
3 Drilling machines use a twist drill to make circular holes. ____
4 Milling machines can only be manually operated. ____
5 Grinding machines remove excessive material from parts. ____
6 Band saws use a band of metal with teeth to cut various parts. ____
7 Presses are not dangerous if operated by both hands. ____

Milling machine

This cuts flat metal surfaces. The piece is fed against a rotating cutting tool. Cutters of many shapes and sizes are available for a wide variety of milling operations. Milling machines may be manually operated, mechanically automated, or digitally automated via computer numerical control (CNC).

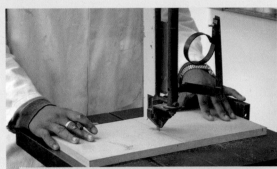

Grinding machine

This removes excessive material from parts that are brought into contact with a rotating abrasive wheel. Grinding is the most accurate of all the basic machining processes, but also the most time consuming.

Press

This is a machine tool that changes the shape of a workpiece. Historically, metal was shaped by hand using a hammer. Machine presses can be dangerous.
Bi-manual controls (controls which require both hands to be on the buttons to operate) are a very good way to prevent accidents.

Band saw

It is a power tool which uses a **blade** consisting of a continuous band of metal with teeth along one edge. The band usually rides on two wheels rotating in the same plane. Band saws are used for woodworking, metalworking, or for cutting a variety of other materials, and are particularly useful for cutting irregular or curved shapes. A constant flow of liquid is poured over the blade to keep it **cool** and preventing it from **overheating**.

3 🎧 4 **Read the text about CNC and put the sentences in the correct order.**

Computer Numerical control (CNC) refers to the automation of machine tools in manufacturing processes. The machines are controlled by computer software which carries out a series of operations automatically. The first NC machines were built in the 1940s and 1950s. They are used to cut and shape products, such as automobile parts that need precise specifications. Parts must be carefully **planned** and prepared by CNC **programmers**. First they view the three-dimensional computer aided designed part. Then they calculate where to cut, the speed and shape and select the tools and materials. The CNC programmers translate the planned machine operations into a set of instructions. These instructions are translated into a computer aided manufacturing (CAM) program containing a set of commands for the machine. The commands are a series of numbers which explains where to cut and the position of material. The computer checks all the operations made by the machine tools.

a ☐ The planned machine operations are translated into a set of instructions.
b ☐ These instructions are translated into a CAM program.
c ☐ The program contains a set of commands for the machine.
d ☐ It is calculated where to cut and tools and materials are selected.
e ☐ The computer checks all the operations made by the machine tools.
f ☐ Programmers view the part in its three-dimensional computer aided design.

The lathe

An example of a machine tool is the lathe, which is a turning machine. **Turning**, one of the most important operations in a machine shop, is a form of material removal process, which is used to create rotational parts by cutting away unwanted material. Usually, the term turning is reserved for the generation of **external** surfaces by this cutting action, whereas when this same essential cutting action is applied to **internal** surfaces (that is, holes of one kind or another) it is called **boring**.

The starting material is generally a workpiece generated by other processes such as casting, forging and extrusion.

Turning can be done manually, in a traditional form of lathe, which frequently requires continuous supervision by the operator, or by using an automated lathe which does not. Today, the most common type of such automation is **computer numerical control**, better known as CNC, which is also commonly used with many other types of machining besides turning.

A lathe rotates the workpiece on its axis to perform various operations. It generally has a **stand** which sits on the floor and elevates the lathe bed to a working height. Small lathes sit on a **workbench**, and do not have a stand. Almost all lathes have a **bed**, which is a horizontal beam. At one end of the bed there is a **headstock** which contains high-precision spinning bearings. Within the bearings there is a rotating horizontal axle, with an axis parallel to the bed, called the **spindle**. Spindles are powered, and impart motion to the workpiece. The spindle is driven, either by foot power or by a belt and gear drive, to a **power source**. In most modern lathes this power source is an integral electric motor. The counterpoint to the headstock is the **tailstock**, also referred to as the loose head because it can be positioned at any convenient point on the bed by undoing a locking nut, sliding it along the required area and then locking it again.

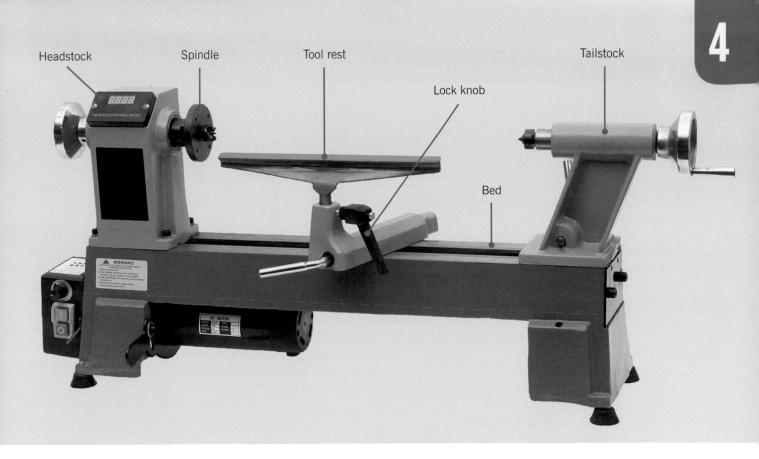

Headstock   Spindle   Tool rest   Lock knob   Tailstock   Bed

4 **Read the text, look at the picture of the lathe above and complete the text with the missing words.**

The horizontal beam is called (**1**) _____. At one end of the bed is the (**2**) _____ which contains high-precision spinning bearings. Rotating within the bearings there is the (**3**) _____. The counterpoint to the (**4**) _____ is the (**5**) _____ which contains a barrel which does not rotate, but can slide in and out. Between the (**6**) _____ and the (**7**) _____ there is a toolpost, at the top of which there is a horizontal (**8**) _____.

5 **Translate these words into your own language.**

1 surface _____
2 hole _____
3 spindle _____
4 lathe bed _____
5 headstock _____

6 tailstock _____
7 saddle _____
8 boring _____
9 casting _____
10 forging _____

6 **Read the text again and match the two parts of the sentences.**

1 The turning process is mainly used
2 A headstock is placed
3 The tailstock, or loose head, is
4 The spindle rotates within
5 Turning is

a a form of material removal process.
b the counterpoint to the headstock.
c at one end of the bed.
d the bearings with a horizontal axe.
e to shape round pieces of metal.

MY GLOSSARY

band saw /bænd sɔː/ _____
blade /bleɪd/ _____
cool /kuːl/ _____
drilling machine /drɪlɪŋ məˈʃiːn/ _____
feature /fiːtʃə(r)/ _____
grinding machine /ˈɡraɪndɪŋ məˈʃiːn/ _____
hole /həʊl/ _____
lathe /leɪð/ _____
machine tool /məˈʃiːn tuːl/ _____

overheating /əʊvəˈhiːtɪŋ/ _____
press /pres/ _____
programmer /ˈprəʊɡræmə(r)/ _____
shaper /ˈʃeɪpə(r)/ _____
skilled /skɪld/ _____
steam engine /stiːm ˈendʒɪn/ _____
stroke /strəʊk/ _____
turning machine /tɜːnɪŋ məˈʃiːn/ _____
waterwheel /wɔːtəwiːl/ _____

5 | What is electricity?

1 **Read the text and label the picture with the name of each part.**

> All substances, solids, liquids or gases, are composed of one or more of the chemical elements. Each element is composed of identical atoms.
> Each atom is composed of a small central nucleus consisting of protons and neutrons around which **orbit shells** of electrons. These electrons are very much smaller than protons and neutrons.
> The electrons in the **outermost** shell are called **valence** electrons and the electrical **properties** of the substance depend on the number of these electrons.
> Neutrons have no electric **charge**, but protons have a positive charge while electrons have a negative charge. In some substances, usually metals, the valence electrons are free to move from one atom to another and this is what constitutes an electric current.

2 **Read the text again and complete the sentences with the missing information.**

1 Elements make up _____
2 Identical atoms _____
3 Atoms consist of _____, _____ and _____
4 Inside there are _____ and _____, while outside _____
5 Shells _____
6 Valence electrons _____
7 Neutrons do not have _____
8 Electricity is generated when _____

3 🎧 5 **Listen and complete the text with the missing information.**

Electricity consists of a (1) _____ of free electrons along a conductor. To produce this **current flow**, a generator is placed at the end of the conductor in order to move the (2) _____.

Conductors

Electricity needs a material which allows a current to **pass through** easily, which offers little (3) _____ to the flow and is full of free electrons. This material is called a conductor and can be in the form of a bar, tube or sheet. The most commonly used (4) _____ are wires, available in many sizes and **thicknesses**. They are **coated** with insulating materials such as plastic.

Semiconductors

Semiconductors such as silicon and germanium are used in transistors and their conductivity is **halfway** in between a conductor and an (5) _____.
Small quantities of other substances, called **impurities**, are introduced in the material to (6) _____ the conductivity.

Insulators

A material which contains very (7) _____ electrons is called an insulator. Glass, rubber, dry wood and (8) _____ resist the flow of electric charge, and as such they are good insulating materials.

Increasing Conducting Ability

Conductors
Silver
Copper
Aluminium
Iron
Mercury
Carbon
Water

Semiconductors
Germanium
Silicon

Insulators
Dry air
Wood
Glass
Rubber

4 Read the text again and decide if the following statements are true (T) or false (F), then correct the false ones.

1 A flow of electrons moving inside a conductor creates an electric current. _____
2 A generator is used to move the charges. _____
3 Electrons can easily pass through any material. _____
4 Any material is a good conductor. _____
5 Conductors are coated with insulators. _____
6 The presence of free electrons affects the conductivity of materials. _____
7 Impurities are introduced to increase conductivity. _____
8 Insulating materials resist the flow of electrons. _____

5 Read the text and complete the table with the missing information.

There are two types of current: Direct current (DC) and Alternating current (AC).
Direct current is a continuous flow of electrons in one direction and it never changes its direction until the power is stopped or **switched off**.
Alternating current constantly changes its direction because of the way it is generated. The term 'frequency' is used to indicate how many times the current changes its direction in one second.
Alternating current has a great advantage over direct current because it can be transmitted over very long distances through small wires, by making energy high voltage and low current.
There are several quantities that are important when we are talking about electric current. Volts (V) – so **named**

after the Italian physicist Alessandro Volta – measure the difference of electric potential between two points on a conducting wire. Amperes (A) measure the amount of current flowing through a conductor, that is to say the number of electrons passing a point in a conductor in one second.
Coulomb (C) measure the quantity of charge transferred in one second by a **steady** current of one ampere. Power is the rate at which work is performed and it is measured in watts (W). A Kilowatt (kW), which is equal to one thousand watts, is used to measure the amount of used or available energy. The amount of electrical energy consumed in one hour at the constant rate of one kilowatt is called kilowatt-hour.

Unit of measurement	What does it measure?
(1) _____	the number of electrons passing a given point in a conductor in one second
(2) _____	the quantity of electricity transferred by a steady current of one ampere
(3) _____	the amount of electric energy used
(4) _____	the difference of potential between two points on a conductor
(5) _____	rate at which work is done

MY GLOSSARY

charge /tʃɑːdʒ/ _____
coated /ˈkəʊtɪd/ _____
conductor /kənˈdʌktə(r)/ _____
current flow /ˈkʌrnt fləʊ/ _____
halfway /hɑːfweɪ/ _____
impurity /ɪmˈpjʊərɪti/ _____
insulator /ɪnsjʊleɪtə(r)/ _____
to name after /tə neɪm ˈɑːftə(r)/ _____
to orbit /tuː ˈɔːbɪt/ _____

to pass through /tə pɑːs θruː/ _____
property /ˈprɒpəti/ _____
semiconductor /semikənˈdʌktə(r)/ _____
shell /ʃel/ _____
steady /ˈstedi/ _____
to switch off /tə swɪtʃ ɒf/ _____
thickness /ˈθɪknəs/ _____
valence /ˈvæləns/ _____

6 Electric circuits

1 Read the text and label the picture with the name of each part.

An electric circuit or network is a pathway through which the electric current can flow. A simple circuit consists of a **power source**, two conducting wires, each one attached to a terminal of the source and a **device** through which electricity can flow. This device is called a **load** and it's attached to the wires. If all the parts are properly connected, the current flows and the lamp lights up. This kind of circuit is called 'closed'.

On the contrary, if the wires are disconnected the circuit is called 'open' or 'broken'. The circuit can be opened and closed by a device called a **switch**.

Loads can **turn** electrical energy **into** a more useful form. Some examples are:

■ **light bulbs**, which change electrical energy into light energy;

■ electric motors, which change electrical energy into mechanical energy;

■ **speakers**, which change energy into sound.

The source provides the electrical energy used by the load. It can be a storage battery or a generator. The switch interrupts the current delivered to the load by the source and allows us to control the flow.

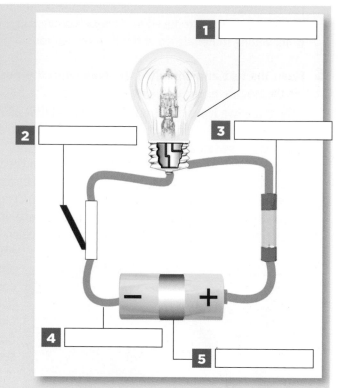

When an abnormally high amount of current passes through a network, you get a **short circuit**. This may occur when there is a drop in the **resistance** or a broken insulation. In order to **prevent** short circuits, it is best to use **fuses**, which **melt** when too much current flows through them, interrupting in this way the circuit.

2 Match the words with their definitions.

1 load
2 switch
3 source
4 fuse
5 closed circuit
6 broken circuit

a ☐ a device which interrupts the circuit
b ☐ a circuit in which wires are disconnected
c ☐ a device which provides power
d ☐ a complete circuit with no breaks at all
e ☐ a device which consumes electric power
f ☐ a protective device

3 Read the text again and answer the following questions.

1 What does a simple circuit consist of?
2 What happens to the lamp in a closed circuit?
3 Can you name some examples of loads?
4 What is a generator?

5 What is the function of a switch?
6 When does a short circuit occur?
7 What can we use to prevent short circuits?
8 How does a fuse work?

4 🎧 6 **Complete the texts with the words in the box. Then listen and check.**

~~components~~	current	turn on	branch	amount
positive	appliances	continue	burns out	path

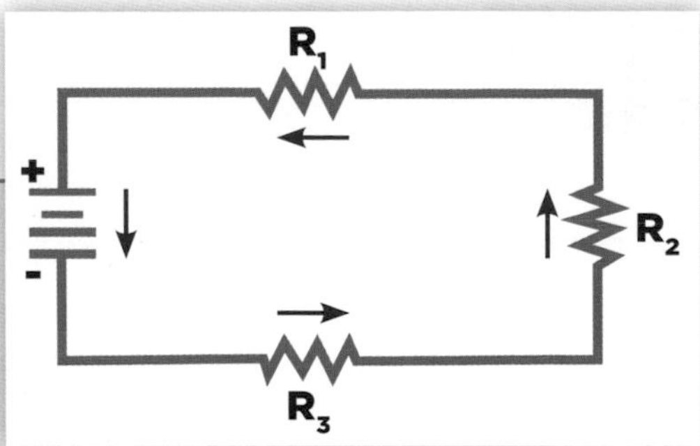

The (1) *components* of a circuit can be wired in two different ways: series or parallel. If components are **arranged** one after another to form a single (2) _____ between the terminals and the components, the circuit is known as a **series circuit**. In this type of circuit, the (3) _____ flows from the negative terminal to the (4) _____ terminal, passing through all the other components of the circuit. This means that the (5) _____ of energy passing through all the components in the series is the same. The main disadvantage of a series circuit is that when a single component in the path (6) _____, the entire circuit stops operating (e.g. Christmas tree lights).

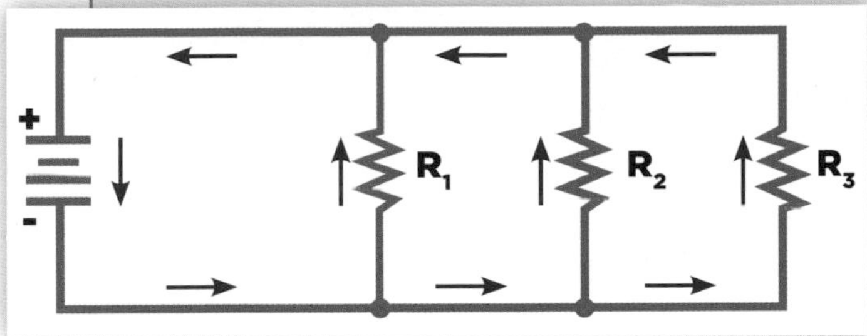

A **parallel circuit** consists of several paths connecting the different components. Each separate path is called a (7) _____ of the circuit. Current from the source divides and flows through the different **branches**. Unlike series circuits, if one of the components in the parallel circuit **burns out**, the other paths (8) _____ to operate. Parallel circuits are commonly used to connect (9) _____ at home, so that each **socket** can function independently.

For example, you don't have to (10) _____ the light in your room for the TV socket to work.

5 **Read the text and find synonyms for the words below.**

A fuse can be added to an electric circuit to protect it from the effects of **undue** power. This safety device, which is made of a heat-sensitive alloy, is connected in series with the circuit it has to protect. If an excessive amount of current flows through the circuit, the alloy will liquefy and open the circuit. A circuit breaker is fundamental in a house to protect circuits against overloading, overheating and short circuits. The advantage of a circuit breaker is that it can be reset after the overloading by replacing the fuse. A professional electrician should always provide his customers with a map of the electric circuit in the house so that it will be easier to work on it in case of **faults**.

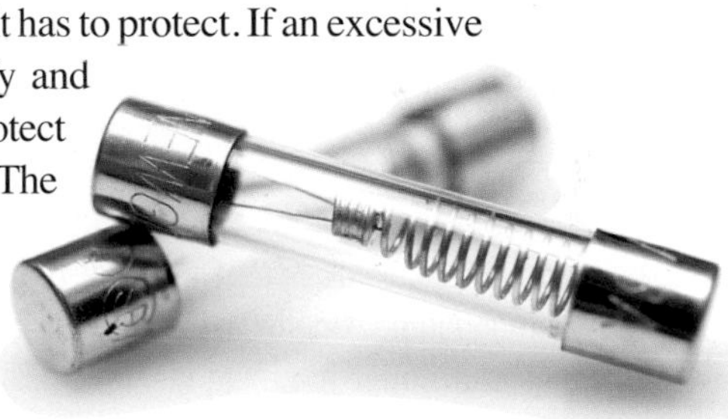

1 excessive: _____
2 reacting to high temperatures: _____
3 to melt: _____
4 loading up: _____
5 adjusted: _____
6 clients: _____

MY GLOSSARY

to arrange /tu: ə'reɪndʒ/ _____
branch /brɑːntʃ/ _____
to burn out /tə bɜːn aʊt/ _____
device /dɪ'vaɪs/ _____
fault /fɒlt/ _____
fuse /fjuːz/ _____
light bulb /laɪt bʌlb/ _____
load /ləʊd/ _____
to melt /tə melt/ _____
parallel circuit /pærəlel 'sɜːkɪt/ _____

power source /paʊə(r) sɔːs/ _____
to prevent /tə prɪ'vent/ _____
series circuit /sɪəriːz 'sɜːkɪt/ _____
short circuit /ʃɔːt 'sɜːkɪt _____
socket /sɒkɪt/ _____
speaker /spiːkə(r)/ _____
switch /swɪtʃ/ _____
to turn into /tə tɜːn 'ɪntuː/ _____
undue /ʌn'djuː/ _____

How energy is produced

Conventional power plants

1 Have you ever wondered where the electricity in your house comes from? Read the texts about the different types of power plants and match them with the pictures.

1 ☐ Nuclear power plants

About 10% of the world's electric power is produced by nuclear power plants. Nuclear power **requires** little **fuel** and causes much less air **pollution** than other power plants, but it can cause severe health and environmental problems when accidents **occur**, with a consequent release of radioactive material. This type of energy is produced by the **splitting** of atoms of uranium, which **releases** heat. This process – called fission – produces large amounts of **steam**, which is used to turn the **blades** of **turbines** thus creating energy. The main problems with nuclear power are linked to the location of the power plants, as people are not **willing** to have these plants near their homes, and the disposal of **waste** material, which stays radioactive for centuries.

2 ☐ Thermoelectric power plants

They provide about $^2/_3$ of the world's electricity. These plants burn fossil fuels, such as coal, oil or natural gas, which are all non-**renewable** resources. This means that in the future there will be a limited **supply** of these resources. The main advantage of thermoelectric power plants is that they are **reliable** and can meet the demand in peak periods. Electricity is generated by heating water in a **boiler** to create steam, which is then pressurised and used to turn the blades of giant turbines that produce electricity. These power plants cause environmental pollution because of the combustion of fossil fuels which release carbon dioxide.

3 ☐ Hydroelectric power plants

The energy produced by water can be captured and turned into electricity. The use of a **dam** on a river allows hydroelectric power plants to store water in an artificial lake, or reservoir. When released, the force of the water spins the blades of giant turbines, which are connected to a generator producing energy. Hydropower is one of the most important renewable energy resources, because it is reliable, efficient and does not pollute the air. Although it has high initial costs, it is cheap to operate. Unfortunately, it has a great impact on the **environment**, as humans, animals and plants may lose their natural habitats.

2 Read the texts again and decide if the following sentences are true (T) or false (F), then correct the false ones.

1 Nuclear power plants do not produce air pollution at all. ____
2 Accidents in nuclear power plants can have terrible consequences for the environment. ____
3 Nuclear power plants produce biodegradable waste material. ____
4 Thermoelectric power is generated by the combustion of renewable resources. ____
5 Thermoelectric power plants are environmentally friendly. ____
6 Dams are built on rivers to store water. ____
7 The water released from the reservoir flows through the generator. ____
8 The only disadvantage of hydropower is its high initial cost. ____

Alternative power sources

3 Read the texts about alternative power sources and complete the table with the missing information.

Environmental problems such as the **greenhouse effect** and air pollution have led scientists to find alternative power sources which are renewable and less polluting.

SOLAR ENERGY
Sunlight can be directly converted into electricity by solar cells made of silicon. When light strikes the cells, a part of it is absorbed by the semiconductor material. The energy of the absorbed light **knocks** electrons loose, allowing them to flow freely and produce electricity. The process of converting light (photons) into electricity (voltage) is known as the photo-voltaic process (PV). Solar cells are usually combined into panels and grouped into **arrays**. Even if the initial costs can be high, the PV system provides an independent, reliable electrical power source. It can produce energy for more than 15 years and its routine **maintenance** is simple and cheap.

WIND ENERGY
Wind energy is one of the cheapest renewable technologies available today. The wind turns the blades of giant turbines, producing in this way kinetic energy which is then converted into mechanical power and electricity by a generator. The main disadvantage of wind energy is that there are few suitable wind sites where it is possible to have a constant production of electricity.

TIDAL ENERGY
This alternative power source, which is typically used in coastal areas, turns the potential energy of **tides** into electricity. Tidal power generators use rising and falling tides in much the same manner as hydroelectric power plants. Large underwater turbines are placed in areas with high tidal movements and are designed to capture the kinetic energy of rising and falling tides. The turbines are driven by the power of the sea both when the tide comes in and when it goes out. The problem with tidal power is that only massive increases in tides can produce energy and there are very few places where this occurs. Moreover, the aquatic ecosystem and the **shoreline** can be **damaged** by the changes in the tidal flow.

GEOTHERMAL ENERGY
In the past, people used **hot springs** for bathing, cooking and heating. Geothermal energy is based on the fact that the Earth is hotter below the surface. The hot water which is stored in the Earth can be brought to the surface and used to drive turbines to produce electricity or it can be **piped** through houses as heat. This energy is cheap and has a low impact on the environment, but there are few sites where it can be extracted at low cost.

BIOMASS ENERGY
Biomass is a renewable energy source deriving from plant material and animal waste. When it is burnt, it releases its chemical energy as heat. Biomass fuels include forest residues (such as dead trees, branches and tree **stumps**), **straw**, **manure** and even municipal solid waste. Biomass energy is a natural process, it is carbon neutral and has low initial costs. It used to be the main source of heating at home in the past and it continues to be highly exploited in the developing world. The main disadvantage of biomass is that it has a smaller potential than other energy sources and requires excellent maintenance skills.

Type of energy	How it works	Advantages	Disadvantages
			high initial costs
Wind energy			
		It is a natural process because it exploits the potential energy of tides.	

4 Match the words with their definitions.

1	array	a ☐	a spot where hot water comes up naturally from the ground
2	kinetic	b ☐	unwanted material left after using
3	tide	c ☐	a group of things arranged in a particular way
4	hot spring	d ☐	waste material from animals used as fertiliser
5	to pipe	e ☐	the process of keeping something in good condition by regularly checking it
6	manure	f ☐	produced by motion
7	waste	g ☐	to send a liquid or a gas through a tube
8	maintenance	h ☐	the regular change in the level of the sea caused by gravitational attraction of the moon and the sun

5 🎧 7 **Read the text about the electrical distribution system and complete it with the words in the box. Then listen and check.**

> pole   demand   lower voltages   consumers   high-voltage
> power plants   delivery   appliances   **network**   transformer

Electricity distribution is the final stage in the (1) _____ of electricity to end users. In order to be able to use electric power for our daily activities, electricity must be transmitted from the (2) _____ to other areas where it can be distributed to different (3) _____.
The electricity generated by power plants is increased or **stepped up** at substations and distributed through (4) _____ transmission lines, in order to minimize energy **losses** and to economise on the material needed for conductors. Transmission lines use voltages as high as 765,000 volts and they are usually connected in a (5) _____. This means that if a station receives an unexpected (6) _____ for electric power, it can call on the other stations to help to meet the demand.
Then electrical power is converted from high voltage to (7) _____ thanks to step-down transformers which turn electricity into different power levels. Once it is sent to your neighbourhood, another small (8) _____ mounted on a (9) _____ converts the power to even lower levels to be used at home. The final voltage is between 110 volts – for lights, TVs, and other smaller appliances – and 240 volts for larger (10) _____.

6 Reorder the different stages in the distribution system and match them to the numbers in the picture.

a ☐ Transmission lines carry high-voltage electricity to different substations.
b ☐ Electricity leaves the power plant.
c ☐ Electricity is **stepped down** by transformers.
d ☐ Current at lower voltages is transmitted to homes and offices.
e ☐ The voltage is increased at a step-up station.
f ☐ Power levels are lowered by small transformers mounted on poles.

7 Read the text again and match each sentence with its ending.

1 Power plants generate
2 Transmission lines are used
3 High voltages mean
4 Step-down transformers
5 Substations can help each other
6 The current transmitted by poles

a ☐ convert electricity from high voltage levels to lower levels.
b ☐ in case of an expected demand for electric power.
c ☐ a reduction in energy losses during transmission.
d ☐ power and distribute it to substations.
e ☐ can be safely used in businesses and homes.
f ☐ to distribute high-voltage electricity to a network of substations.

8 Pairwork What is your opinion on energy saving? What do you and your family usually do to save energy? Take this test and discuss your answers in pairs.

1 I turn my desk lamp on only when it's dark.   Yes ☐ No ☐

2 I try to open the fridge as little as possible.   Yes ☐ No ☐

3 I don't use the lift to go down the stairs.   Yes ☐ No ☐

4 My parents take the bus to work instead of driving.   Yes ☐ No ☐

5 Our house temperature is below 20°C.   Yes ☐ No ☐

6 I always turn the light off when I leave a room.   Yes ☐ No ☐

7 I turn the TV off if I am not watching it.   Yes ☐ No ☐

8 We try not to use air conditioning unless it's very hot.   Yes ☐ No ☐

9 We use rechargeable batteries.   Yes ☐ No ☐

10 We use energy-saving light bulbs.   Yes ☐ No ☐

MY GLOSSARY

array /əˈreɪ/ _____
biomass /ˈbaɪəʊmæs/ _____
blade /bleɪd/ _____
boiler /ˈbɔɪlə(r)/ _____
dam /dæm/ _____
to damage /tə ˈdæmɪdʒ/ _____
environment /ɪnˈvaɪərənmənt/ _____
fuel /fjʊəl/ _____
greenhouse /ˈgriːnhaʊs/ _____
hot spring /hɒt ˈsprɪŋ/ _____
to knock /tə nɒk/ _____
loss /lɒs/ _____
maintenance /ˈmeɪntənənts/ _____
manure /məˈnjʊə(r)/ _____
network /ˈnetwɜːk/ _____
to occur /tuː əˈkɜː(r)/ _____
piped /paɪpt/ _____
pollution /pəˈluːʃn/ _____

power plants /ˈpaʊə(r) plɑːnts/ _____
to release /tə rɪˈliːs/ _____
reliable /rɪˈlaɪəbl/ _____
renewable /rɪˈnjuːəbl/ _____
to require /tə rɪˈkwaɪə(r)/ _____
shoreline /ˈʃɔːlaɪn/ _____
splitting /ˈsplɪtɪŋ/ _____
steam /stiːm/ _____
to step down /tə step daʊn/ _____
to step up /tə step ʌp/ _____
straw /strɔː/ _____
stump /stʌmp/ _____
supply /səˈplaɪ/ _____
tide /taɪd/ _____
turbine /ˈtɜːbaɪn/ _____
waste /weɪst/ _____
willing /ˈwɪlɪŋ/ _____

8 What is electronics?

1 Read the text about the main inventions in electronics and complete the table with the missing information.

Electronics is the **branch** of science which controls electricity in order to **convey** a **signal** using semiconductor materials. These signals represent numbers, letters, sounds, pictures, computer instructions or other information. Radio systems were developed to read and understand these signals and in 1920 radio **broadcasting** started, making it possible for electromagnetic **waves** to travel long distances.

More sophisticated devices were needed during the Second World War and the invention of radar (Radio Detection and Ranging) represented a **further** step in electronics, making it possible to determine the altitude, direction and speed of moving and fixed objects.

The invention of television in the 1920s was one of the most revolutionary and popular inventions in history and it showed the importance of electronics in certain branches of industry. For the first time in history it became possible to transmit images and sound over wire circuits.

The first computer appeared in 1946. This machine, which could solve a wide range of computing problems, was built over a period of three years by a team of American scientists working at the University of Pennsylvania. It was a **huge** machine weighing almost 50 tons.

The first transistor was assembled in 1957 by a team of scientists working at the Bell Laboratories in the U.S.A, and it was a real coming of age in the science of electronics because it replaced the use of valves. Transistors are very small, easy to handle, cheap, and they use little power.

The silicon chip – which followed the transistor in the 1960s – can contain up to several thousand transistors packed and interconnected in **layers** beneath the surface. It is really **tiny** (usually less than one centimetre square and about half a millimetre thick) and it has **paved the way** to microelectronics.

Electronics has influenced and improved the way information is stored, processed and distributed. Social and personal life has been deeply affected by these inventions and many financial, business, medical, education and political routines have been **speeded up**.

Invention	Year	Function
		read and understand electronic signals
Radar		
	1920s	

2 Writing Think of an electronic device (TV, radio, mobile phone, computer, etc.) you use every day. Write about its use, advantages, disadvantages and your opinion of it. Write about 60 words.

Electronic circuits

3 **Read the text about the different kinds of electronic circuits and answer the questions.**

A conventional electronic circuit is made of separate components attached to a base called a printed circuit board (PCB). Before being finalised and manufactured, the electronic circuit must be tested many times on an experimentation board called a **breadboard**. It consists of a perforated block of plastic with several **spring clips** connected by copper wires. It doesn't require **soldering** as its components can be pushed straight into the holes, so it is easy to change connections and replace pieces. It is generally used to create temporary **prototypes** and experiment with circuit design.

The integrated circuit, also known as a chip, is one of the most important inventions of the 20th century. Integrated circuits are used in almost all electronic equipment today, for example watches, calculators and microprocessors. It consists of millions of transistors and other electronic components combined to form a complex set on a thin **slice** of silicon or other semiconductor material. Chips are becoming tinier and tinier and they are produced in large quantities so that costs are reduced. Since signals have to travel a short distance, they work faster, consume less power and generate less heat. They are also more reliable given the limited amount of connections which could fail.

The microprocessor is the heart of any normal computer: it is a logic integrated circuit chip which can carry out a sequence of operations when it receives instructions from different input devices. As it doesn't contain a large memory, it can't work alone but needs to be supported by other integrated circuits to be connected with **peripherals**. Most microprocessors are found inside computers and are called the CPU (Central Processing Unit). In order to work properly, the microprocessor needs to receive instructions from a memory chip. These instructions are then **decoded**, executed and elaborated so as to get the results available. The most sophisticated microprocessors can contain up to 10 million transistors and run 300 million cycles per second. It means that the computer can perform about a billion instructions every second. As technology continues to evolve, microprocessors are becoming tinier and tinier.

1 What is a conventional circuit made of?
2 What does PCB stand for?
3 What is a breadboard?
4 What does a chip consist of?
5 What is a chip made out of?

6 What are the advantages of chips compared to conventional electronic circuits?
7 What is a microprocessor?
8 How many instructions can computers perform?

4 **Read the text again and match the words with their definitions.**

1 prototype
2 perforated
3 soldering
4 to fail
5 peripheral
6 to decode

a ☐ to convert an electrical signal into another code
b ☐ the act of joining metallic parts
c ☐ an original model used to test a circuit or a product
d ☐ to perform ineffectively
e ☐ having a series of holes
f ☐ an auxiliary device that works with a computer

8

5 🎧 8 **Read the text about mobile phones and complete it with the words in the box. Then listen and check.**

> cell   lines   microprocessor   photos   radio   signals
> flash   emails   antenna   movement

A cellular phone (or mobile phone) is designed to give the user freedom of (1) _____ while using a telephone. It uses (2) _____ signals to communicate between the phone and the (3) _____. The server area is divided into smaller areas called cells and an antenna is placed within each cell and connected by telephone (4) _____. These lines connect cellular phones to one another: a computer selects the antenna closest to the telephone when a call is made. If the phone moves to one serving (5) _____ to another, the radio signal is transferred to the actual cell without interrupting the conversation.

The circuit board is the heart of the system. A chip translates the **outgoing** and **incoming** (6) _____ from analogue to digital and back from digital to analogue. The (7) _____ handles all the functions for the keyboard, the display and the loudspeakers, and it controls the signal to the base station.

Other (8) _____ memory chips provide storage for the **operating system**.

A cellular phone is not only a phone but it provides an incredible amount of functions:

- store information;
- use a calculator;
- send and receive (9) _____;
- surf the Internet;
- play simple games;
- play music, take (10) _____ and videos.

Can you imagine your life without your mobile phone?

6 Pairwork Decide if the following statements are true (T) or false (F).

1 Mobile phones use radio signals to communicate. _____
2 The server area is divided into smaller areas called stations. _____
3 An antenna is placed every two or three cells. _____
4 Communication with a mobile within a cell is independent from the base station. _____
5 There are interruptions when you move to one cell to another. _____
6 The antenna is the heart of the system. _____
7 The signal must be translated. _____
8 The flash memory handles all the functions. _____
9 Loudspeakers are controlled by the microprocessor. _____
10 You can text and send emails with your mobile phone. _____

MY GLOSSARY

branch /brɑːntʃ/ _____
breadboard /ˈbredbɔːd/ _____
broadcasting /ˈbrɔːdkɑːstɪŋ/ _____
to convey /tə kənˈveɪ/ _____
to decode /tə diːˈkəʊd/ _____
further /ˈfɜːðə(r)/ _____
huge /hjuːdʒ/ _____
incoming /ˈɪnkʌmɪŋ/ _____
layer /ˈleɪə(r)/ _____
operating system /ˈɒpəreɪtɪŋ ˈsɪstəm/ _____

outgoing /aʊtˈgəʊɪŋ/ _____
to pave the way /tə peɪv ðə weɪ/ _____
peripheral /pəˈrɪfərəl/ _____
signal /ˈsɪgnəl/ _____
slice /slaɪs/ _____
soldering /ˈsəʊldərɪŋ/ _____
to speed up /tə spiːd ʌp/ _____
spring clip /sprɪŋ klɪp/ _____
tiny /ˈtaɪni/ _____
wave /weɪv/ _____

Telecommunications and networks

Communication has always played a crucial role in human societies and over time its forms have evolved through the progression of technology, transforming itself into telecommunication. The telegraph, the telephone, the radio, the television, the radar, the fax and, more recently, the computer are all devices which were invented to communicate using electromagnetic waves. Thanks to them, we can transmit texts, pictures, sounds and images and reach everyone in any part of the world.

1 Pairwork **Look at the following means of communication and take turns asking and answering the following questions.**

How often do you use them?
What do you use them for?
Who do you use them with?
What are their advantages?
Can you think of any risk connected with their use?

2 **Look at the diagram and complete the text about telecommunication systems.**

MEANS OF TRANSMISSION

- cables
  - wires
  - coaxial cables
  - optical fibres
- radio waves
  - antennas
  - satellites

Telecommunication systems need means for the (1) _____ of any information, which is translated into electromagnetic waves that connect the **transmitter** to the **receiver**. These means can be physical media, such as (2) _____, or radio (3) _____, which are transmitted by air. Different kind of cables can be used. The simplest communication cables consist of a single pair of (4) _____ **twisted** together. Other types are (5) _____ cables and optical (6) _____. Radio waves need (7) _____ to be transmitted and sometimes (8) _____ are necessary for long-distance transmission.

3 Read the text about the different kinds of transmission media and complete the table.

Ground transmission

Wires provide a cheap and effective means of communication that was predominant in the past. Wires, which are made out of copper and insulated with plastic, can be single or twisted, and they are used mainly in telephone and computer networks.

Coaxial cables consist of an **inner** conductor insulated with plastic and **surrounded** by a **woven** copper **shield**. They are used in television and radio as these cables can support about 60 channels. The inner copper cable is insulated to protect the wires from **bending** and crushing and to reduce the noises.

Optical fibres are used in place of simple copper wires to carry larger amounts of information. They consist of **strands** of pure glass as thin as a human hair. Signals travel along fibres with less loss and without any electromagnetic interference. As they permit transmission over longer distances and at a higher speed, they are used in communication systems, in some medical instruments and in a wide variety of **sensing devices**.

Air transmission

Antennas were invented to capture radio signals and convert them into electrical signals through the receiver. They can also receive electrical signals from the transmitter and convert them into radio signals.

These electric devices, which provide information at a cheap rate, are essential to all equipment that uses radio. They are used in systems such as radio and television broadcasting, radar, mobile phones, and satellite communications, for which they are in form of **dishes**.

Satellites are machines launched into space to move around Earth or another celestial body. A communications satellite is basically a station which receives signals in a given frequency and then retransmits them at a different frequency to avoid interference problems. The first satellite was launched by the Soviet Union in 1957. There are different types of satellites: low-orbit satellites, which travel at about 300 km from the Earth and observe the planet, providing accurate information about agriculture, pollution and weather **forecasting**; medium-altitude satellites, which travel at about 9000-18000 km from the Earth and are used in telecommunications.

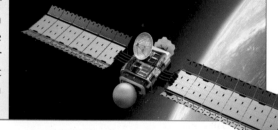

Means of transmission	Material	Function	Type of signal (ground or air)	Advantages
wires				
coaxial cables				
optical fibres				
antennas				
satellites				

4 Read the text about networks and answer the questions.

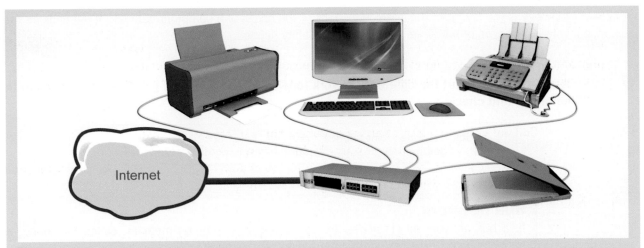

A network is a group of computers **linked** together. It consists of at least two computers joined by cables on the same desk or same office, but it can also mean thousands of computers across the world. The users of a network can **share** hardware (scanner, printer, fax machine, etc.), access data in other people's computers and run other programs stored in the network although not installed on their own computer.

A network consists of:
- nodes, that is to say different computers and devices;
- a connecting medium, such as cables or a wireless connection;
- routers, which are special computers enabled to send messages;
- switches, that is to say devices which help to select a specific path to follow.

Networks can be connected in different ways according to the area they cover.
A LAN (Local Area Network) is generally located in a limited space, such as a building or a campus.
On the contrary, a WAN (Wide Area Network) operates in a larger area and it can reach most of the world, so it could be described as a collection of LANs all over the world.

The exchange of information in a network is controlled by communications protocols, which define the formats and rules that computers must follow when talking to one another.
Well-known communications protocols are Ethernet, which is a family of protocols used in LANs, and the Internet Protocol Suite, which is used in any computer network.

Computer networks offer many advantages. For example, they facilitate communication, allowing people to send emails and texts, make phone/video calls and videoconference. Furthermore, networks allow people to share files, data, and other types of information as users may access data and information stored on other computers in the network.

On the other hand, networks may be difficult to set up and may be insecure as computer **hackers** can send viruses or computer worms to the net computer. They may also interfere with other technologies, as power line communication strongly disturbs certain forms of radio communication and access technology such as ADSL.

1 What does a network consist of?
2 What is a router?
3 What is a LAN?
4 What is a WAN?

5 What is the function of communications protocols?
6 What is Ethernet used for?
7 What are the advantages of using a network?
8 What are the disadvantages of using a network?

5 Writing Refer back to the text and write a summary of the components, pros and cons of networks and describe a situation in which a network can be very useful.

Network topologies

A network topology is the layout of the interconnections of the nodes of a computer network. It depends on the distance involved, the type of hardware used and the stability needed.

6 🎧 9 **Read the texts about the different network topologies and fill in the gaps with the words in the box. Then listen and check.**

> nodes   circle   network   pathway   affect   configure
> small   destination   star   failure   exchanging   backbone

Bus network

In a bus network all (1) *nodes* are connected to a common medium, called **backbone**, as it happens with Christmas lights. Information sent along the (2) _____ travels until the destination is reached. This kind of topology is generally used only for (3) _____ networks, as it isn't able to connect a large number of computers. The main advantage offered by this topology is that if a computer or device doesn't work, it doesn't (4) _____ the others.

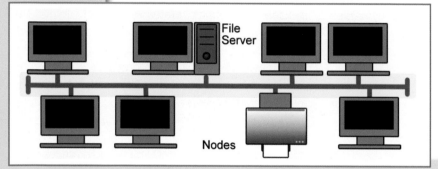

File Server

Nodes

Star network

In a star network all nodes are connected to a special central node called the **hub**. Once it has received a signal, the hub passes it to all the other nodes until it reaches the (5) _____ computer. This means that all the computers and devices are joined together. This topology is commonly used in businesses because it can **grant** rapidity and safety in (6) _____ data. Thanks to this topology, data is always **up-to-date** and if a computer doesn't work, it doesn't affect the others.

The only disadvantage to it is that if the hub goes down, the whole (7) _____ doesn't work.

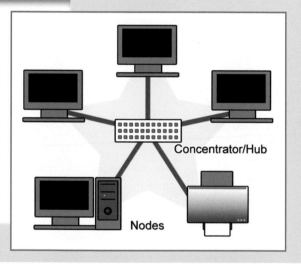

Concentrator/Hub

Nodes

7 **Read the texts again and decide if the following statements are true (T) or false (F), then correct the false ones.**

1 The topology chosen depends only on the location of computers. _____
2 All topologies use many cables and are very expensive. _____
3 In a bus topology all the buses are connected one after the other. _____
4 In a bus topology a server controls the flow of data. _____
5 In a star network data is always updated. _____
6 The hub doesn't connect printers and other devices in a star topology. _____
7 In the ring topology each node is connected to the hub. _____
8 In the ring topology if the hub doesn't work, the network goes down. _____
9 Star bus topology combines elements of bus and ring topologies. _____
10 In a star bus topology a backbone line failure affects the whole network. _____

8 Read the texts again and complete the table with the missing information.

Topology	Connection	Use	Advantages	Disadvantages
		small networks		
	Each node is connected to the central hub.			
ring				

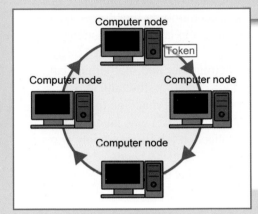

Computer node

Token

Computer node

Computer node

Computer node

Ring network

In a ring network each node is connected to its left in a (8) _____. There is no central hub that holds all the data, and communication is sent in one direction around the ring through the use of a **token**. As it requires fewer cables, this topology is less expensive. Nonetheless, because it provides only one (9) _____ among the nodes, a single node (10) _____ may isolate all the devices attached to the ring.

Star bus topology

Star bus topology is the most common network topology used today. It combines elements of star and bus topologies to create a more effective network. Computers in a specific area are connected to hubs creating a (11) _____, then each hub is connected together along the network backbone.

The main advantage of this type of topology is that it can be more easily expanded over time than a bus or a star. On the other hand, this topology is more difficult to (12) _____ than the others and if the backbone line breaks, the whole network **goes down**.

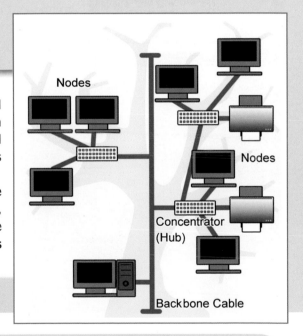

Nodes

Nodes

Concentrator (Hub)

Backbone Cable

The computer evolution

The word computer was first used in 1613 to describe a person who performed calculations, but now the term almost universally refers to automated electronic machinery.

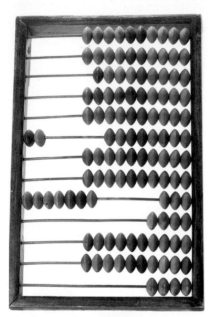

Its history started more than 2000 years ago in Babylonia (Mesopotamia), when the **abacus**, a wooden rack holding two horizontal wires with beads strung on them, came into use. First computers were used primarily for numerical calculations. In the XVI century Leonardo da Vinci drew sketches for a machine that were sufficiently complete and correct for modern engineers to build a calculator on their basis. A century later, in 1623, the first calculator was built by German astronomer and mathematician Wilhelm Schickard, but we have to wait for French mathematician-philosopher Blaise Pascal to see the production of a machine in 1644. It was called **Pascaline**, or Arithmetic Machine, and it was invented for Pascal's father to help him with his tax collection job. It could only perform additions and subtractions. In 1822, Charles Babbage began developing the Difference Engine, considered the first mechanical computer or automatic computing engine. Later, in 1837, he proposed the first general mechanical computer, the **Analytical Engine**. The machine was designed to consist of four components: the engine, the store, the reader, and the printer. These elements are the essential components of every computer today. In 1946, nearly a century later, the **ENIAC** (Electronic Numerical Integrator Analyzer and Computer) was built by the United States. It was the first electronic digital computer which was fully functional. It occupied about 1,800 square feet, the size of a large room, and weighed almost 50 tons. This first generation of computers used vacuum tubes, about 18,000 were used for the ENIAC. They could only perform single tasks, and they had no operating system.

The second generation of machines started in the 1950s. They used transistors which were more reliable than vacuum tubes. In 1950, the **UNIVAC 1101** was the first computer capable of storing and running a program from memory. During this generation of computers over 100 computer programming languages were developed.
In 1953 **IBM** publicly introduced the **701**, its first electric and mass-produced computer. The invention of the integrated circuit brought us the third generation of computers.

Computers became smaller, more powerful and more reliable, able to run many different programs at the same time. In 1980 Microsoft Disk Operating System (**MS-Dos**) was launched and in 1981 IBM introduced the personal computer (**PC**) for home and office use. Three years later Apple created the Macintosh computer with its icon driven interface and the 90s gave us Windows operating system. In 2010 the first **iPad**, a tablet computer, was unveiled. As a result of the various improvements to the development of the computer we have seen the computer being used in all areas of life. It is a very useful tool that will continue to experience new development as time passes.

1 Read the text and complete the table with the missing information.

When	What	Who
400 BC		
XVI Century		
1613		
1623		
1644		
1837		
1946		
1953		
1981		
2010		

2 Pairwork **Look at the table in exercise 2. Ask and answer questions about the computer evolution.**

A: When was ENIAC built?
B: It was built in 1946.

3 Read the text about Steve Jobs and complete it with the words from the box.

| Apple | iPad | technological | battle | evolution | products | Macintosh | Computers |

Steve Jobs was born in 1955 in San Francisco, California. At school he showed great (**1**) _____ interests. Jobs experimented with different scientific attempts before starting Apple (**2**)_____ with Steve Wozniak in 1976. Together they created the (**3**)_____ I and Apple II computers. In 1984, the (**4**)_____ computer was launched.
Apple's revolutionary (**5**)_____, which include the iPod, iPhone and (**6**)_____, are now seen as dictating the (**7**)_____ of modern technology. He died in 2011, after a long (**8**) _____ with cancer.

Steve Jobs
1955-2011

11 Computer technology

1 How much do you know about computers? Work in pairs and answer the questions.

1 What is a computer?
2 What does a computer do?
3 What are the main components of a computer?
4 Have you got a computer at home? What type is it?
5 What do you generally use your computer for?

2 Read the text about computer components and complete the table.

A computer is an electronic device that **performs** high-speed mathematical or logical operations and executes instructions in a program. Its main functions are to accept and **process** data to produce results, store information and programs and show results.

The main characteristics of these powerful machines are:
- speed, as they can execute billions of operations per second
- high **reliability** in the elaboration and delivery of data
- **storage** of huge amounts of information

A computer consists of hardware and software. The word hardware refers to all the components you can physically see such as the CPU (Central Processing Unit), the internal memory system, the mass storage system, the peripherals (input and output devices) and the connecting system. Software, instead, comprises all the computer programs and related data that provide the instructions for a computer to work properly.

The CPU is the brains of your computer and consists of ALU (Arithmetic Logic Unit), which carries out the instructions of a program to perform arithmetical and logical operations, and CU (Control Unit), which controls the system and coordinates all the operations. In order to memorise input and output data, there is an internal memory that can be distinguished into volatile and non-volatile. Volatile memory is memory that loses its contents when the computer or hardware device is off. Computer RAM (Random Access Memory) is a good example of volatile memory. It is the main memory of the computer where all data can be stored as long as the machine is on. On the contrary, a non-volatile memory contains information, data and programs that cannot be modified, or can be modified only very slowly and with difficulty. Computer ROM (Read Only Memory), for example, contains essential and permanent information and software which allow the computer to work properly. Memory **storage** devices are available in different options, sizes and capacities. These devices are extremely useful; they can be rewritten and offer incredible storage capacity, up to 256 GB. They can be magnetic (hard disks), optical (CDs and DVDs) or solid (flash memory cards).

Component (acronym)	Full name / Description	Functions and properties
hardware		
software		
CPU		
ALU		
CU		
RAM		
ROM		

Mass storage devices are available in an incredible number of options with different storage capacity up to 256 GB for some portable drives. A very popular type of **removable** device is represented by USB flash drives, which are much smaller and **lighter** than other portable drives, but which can still provide a huge storage capacity.

3 🎧 10 **Read the text about USB flash drives and fill in the gaps with the words in the box. Then listen and check.**

plugged	backup	board	moving	disadvantage
operating system	case	off-site	water	pocket

A USB flash drive is a flash memory data storage device integrated with a USB (Universal Serial Bus) interface. USB flash drives are removable and rewritable, and they're small enough to be carried in a (1) _____. These portable drives are faster, have thousands of times more capacity, and are more durable and reliable than CD-ROMs because of their lack of (2) _____ parts.

Unlike most removable drives, a USB drive does not require **rebooting** after it's attached, they are very robust and use very little power. They just need to be (3) _____ into a USB port to work and they're compatible with any modern (4) _____, such as Linux, Mac OS X and Windows.

A flash drive consists of a small printed circuit (5) _____ carrying the circuit elements and a USB connector, insulated electrically and protected inside a plastic (6) _____.

The drive is often used as a (7) _____ medium to save data, because it is very **user-friendly** and it can be carried (8) _____ for safety despite being large enough for several **backups**. Moreover, flash drives are cheaper and less fragile than many other backup systems. Its only (9) _____ is that it can be easily lost because of its size and it's easy for people without a right to data to take **illicit** backups. Some specially manufactured flash drives are provided with a metal or rubber **case** designed to be **waterproof** and almost unbreakable. It's been tested that these flash drives can **retain** their memory even after being submerged in (10) _____, put in a **washing machine** and run over with a car.

4 **Find the synonyms for the following words in the text.**

1 long-lasting: _____
2 sturdy: _____
3 inserted: _____

4 easy to use: _____
5 fabricated: _____
6 hold: _____

5 **Read the text again and decide if the following statements are true (T) or false (F), then correct the false ones.**

1 Flash drives are provided with a very limited storage capacity. _____
2 They are lighter that other removable drives. _____
3 They need an external power supply to work. _____
4 USB flash drives are compatible with few operating systems. _____
5 A plastic case prevents the printed circuit board from being damaged. _____
6 USB drives are convenient for transferring data between computers or for personal backups. _____
7 They are more expensive than other backup systems. _____
8 Some models continue to work even after being accidentally dropped into water. _____

6 Read the text and complete the definitions with the words in the box.

| mouse | speaker | modem | **keyboard** | **printer** | disk drives | monitor | scanner |

We call hardware the equipment involved in the functioning of a computer. It consists of several components that can either send data to the computer (input devices) or convert and transfer data out of the computer in the form of text, sound, image, or other media (output devices). The main input and output devices are:

(1) _____: this is the display, which helps you control computer operations. It accepts video signals from a computer and shows information on a screen. The first models used cathode ray tubes (CRTs), which was the dominant technology until they were replaced by liquid crystal displays (LCDs) in the 21st Century.

(2) _____: this is like a **typewriter** with an arrangement of **keys** corresponding to written symbols. It is generally used to type text and numbers in a word processor. However there are some special keys or combination of keys which, pressed simultaneously, can produce actions or computer commands.

(3) _____: this is a dynamic pointing device used to move the cursor on the screen. It consists of a plastic case, a little ball that sends impulses to the computer when rolled on a flat surface, one or more buttons, and a cable that connects the device to the computer. Modern computers are provided with built-in pointing devices that let you control the cursor by simply moving your finger over a pad.

(4) _____: this captures images from printed pages or photos and converts them into digital data. They usually come with software that lets you resize or modify a captured image.

(5) _____: this receives text and graphics from a computer and transfers the information to paper. It may vary in size, speed, **sophistication**, and cost. In general, more expensive models are used for higher-resolution colour printing.

(6) _____: this converts electrical signals into sounds and allows you to listen to music, multimedia web sites and conversations with other people.

(7) _____: this is a device or program that enables a computer to transmit data over telephone lines, by converting digital signals into analog waves. It can be either internal or external to your computer.

(8) _____: these are devices that allow you to read and write data on disks. They can be either mounted inside the computer and store the computer operating system and all the documents and programs, or come in the form of removable devices.

7 Pairwork Look at the picture in exercise 6 and decide if the components are input (I) or output (O) devices.

8 Read the descriptions of the different types of computers and match them with the correct picture.

When you go to a computer shop, you can find computers for any use, size or capability.

1 ☐ **Desktop**: this is a personal computer intended for regular use at a single location. It's designed to sit on your desk, and as such it consists of a monitor and a **tower** with extra drives inside.

2 ☐ **Laptop**: this is a portable computer, which integrates all the usual components of a desktop computer into a single unit. Smaller versions of laptops are known as notebooks. It is useful for people who do not have a fixed place to work at. They are lighter and handier than desktop computers, but they also tend to be more expensive. They require an expensive battery that needs to be **recharged** quite often.

3 ☐ **Netbook**: this is a portable computer, with limited capabilities as compared to standard laptops. It is smaller and lighter, but it also has less processing power than a full-sized laptop. It is useful for people who don't have a fixed place to work at or for those who travel, but still need to surf the Net. They use a battery which needs to be recharged often.

4 ☐ **Tablet**: this is a small portable computer designed to have large amounts of information **close to hand**. They are provided with light long lasting batteries and special operating systems. They don't require any keyboard but use touch screens to enter data and access information.

5 ☐ **Mainframe**: this is a very large and expensive computer capable of supporting thousands of users at the same time. For this reason, it is used in businesses and it's the centre of computer networks. These super computers, which are usually as big as a large refrigerator, are the most powerful and expensive ones and they're used for jobs which require enormous amounts of calculations, such as weather forecasting, engineering design and economic data processing.

9 Read the texts again and answer the questions.

1 What does a desktop computer consist of?
2 Are desktop computers designed to be carried around?
3 Who are laptops useful for?
4 What is the difference between a netbook and a laptop?
5 How can you access or enter information on a palmtop?
6 What are mainframes used for?

The Internet

10 Read the text and complete the sentences with the missing information.

The Internet is a worldwide information system consisting of **countless** networks and computers, which allow millions of people to share information and data. Thanks to the Internet it is now possible for people all over the world to communicate with one another in a fast and cheap way.

The Internet was first invented in the 1960s in the USA by the Department of Defence as an internal project to **link** computers. The Department wanted an extremely safe way of sending messages in case of nuclear attack. It was a British physicist, Sir Timothy Berners-Lee, who used it to make information available to everyone and created the most important media of the 21st century. In 1980 while working at CERN in Geneva – the largest particle physics laboratory in the world – he first thought of using hypertext to share and update information among researchers. Then in 1989-90 he produced a plan to link hypertext to the Internet to create the World Wide Web. He designed and built the first site browser and editor, as well as the first web server called httpd (Hypertext Trasfer Protocol Deamon). Hypertext are the words or chains of words in a text we can click on to be linked to new sites whose content is related to the words. But how does this global system work? It is a network of people and information linked together by telephone lines which are connected to computers. The applications are based on a client/server relationship, in which your computer is the client and a remote computer is the server. All you need to join this system is a computer, a normal telephone line, a modem and an account with an Internet Service Provider (ISP), a company that provides access to the Internet. A user buys a **subscription** to a service provider, which gives him/her an identifying username, a password and an email address. With a computer and a modem, the user can connect to the service provider's computer which gives access to many services, such as WWW (world wide web), emails and FTP (file transfer protocol).

1 The Internet allows people to _____

2 In the 1960s, the Internet was used _____

3 Thanks to Sir Timothy Berners-Lee _____

4 He created the World Wide Web by linking _____

5 All you need to access the Internet is _____

6 The ISP is _____

11 Writing Write a summary of the text in exercise 10 following the flow chart.

| Write about the role of the Internet in the modern world. | → | Describe the origins of the Internet and its first uses. | → | Explain the revolution that occurred in the 1990s. | → | Say how the Internet system works. | → | Write about the importance of the Internet in your own life and describe how you use it. |

12 Read the text about the different types of Internet connections and match the words in the box with the correct definition.

> DSL   wireless   satellite   cable   dial-up

1 _____

It used to be the most common way to access the Internet. This type of connection requires you to use a **landline** telephone connection and a modem connected to your computer. In order to establish the connection, you must dial a telephone number provided by the ISP. Nowadays it represents the cheapest but slowest way to connect to the Internet. Another disadvantage of this type of connection is that you cannot make or receive phone calls while connected to the Internet.

2 _____

A digital subscriber line is another way to connect to the Internet through a telephone connection, but the quality and speed of the connection is significantly greater than a dial-up connection. Moreover, unlike a dial-up connection, this connection is always on, which means you can still make and receive telephone calls with your landline telephone.

3 _____

In order to have this type of connection you must subscribe to an account with a local cable television provider and connect a cable modem to your computer. This connection is very fast and doesn't **interfere** with your telephone line.

4 _____

This is one of the newest Internet connection types. This connection does not require your computer to be connected to telephone or cable wires, as it uses radio frequency bands. You simply need a modem and an account with an Internet provider. Nowadays, many coffee shops, restaurants, public libraries and schools offer this type of connection for free. However, it is typically more expensive and mainly available in metropolitan areas.

5 _____

This type of connection allows a user to access the Internet via a satellite that orbits the earth. Because of the enormous distances signals must travel, this connection is slightly slower than terrestrial connections through cables. It represents an excellent option for people living in rural areas where other types of connections are not available.

MY GLOSSARY

backup /ˈbækʌp/ _____
case /keɪs/ _____
close to hand /kləʊs tə hænd/_____
countless /ˈkaʊntləs/ _____
illicit /ɪˈlɪsɪt/ _____
to interfere /tuː ɪntəˈfɪə(r)/ _____
key /kiː/ _____
keyboard /ˈkiː bɔːd/ _____
landline /ˈlændlaɪn/ _____
laptop /ˈlæptɒp/ _____
to link /tə lɪŋk/_____
mainframe /ˈmeɪnfreɪm/ _____
palmtop /ˈpɑːmtɒp/ _____
to perform /tə pəˈfɔːm/ _____
printer /ˈprɪntə(r)/_____

to process /tə ˈprəʊses/ _____
rebooting /riːˈbuːtɪŋ/ _____
to recharge /tə riːˈtʃɑːdʒ/ _____
reliability /rɪˌlaɪəˈbɪlətɪ/_____
removable /rɪˈmuːvəbl̩/ _____
to retain /tə rɪˈteɪn/_____
sophistication /səˌfɪstɪˈkeɪʃn/ _____
storage /ˈstɔːrɪdʒ/ _____
subscription /səbˈskrɪpʃn/ _____
tower /ˈtaʊə(r)/_____
typewriter /ˈtaɪpraɪtə(r)/_____
user-friendly /ˈjuːzəˈfrendli/ _____
washing machine /ˈwɒʃɪŋ məˈʃiːn/ _____
waterproof /ˈwɔːtəpruːf/_____

12 Automation and robotics

1 Read the text about automation and match the words with their definition.

Mechanisation refers to the process of providing human beings with machinery capable of assisting them with the muscular **requirements** of work. A further development of mechanisation is represented by automation, which implies the use of control systems and information technologies to reduce the need for both physical and mental work to produce **goods**.

Automation has had a great impact on industries over the last century, changing the world economy from industrial jobs to service jobs. In **manufacturing**, where the process began, automation has meant that the desired results can be obtained through a series of instructions made automatically by the system, which define the actions to be done. Automated manufacturing grants higher consistency and quality, while reducing **lead times** and **handling**. It also improves **work flow** and increases the morale of workers when a good implementation of the automation is made.

However, the purpose of automation cannot be seen only in terms of a reduction of cost and time; there are several more aspects to be taken into consideration. For example, while it is true that automation offers a higher precision in the manufacturing process, it is also true that it requires skilled workers who can make repairs and manage the machinery.

The following table sums up the main advantages and disadvantages of automation:

Advantages	Disadvantages
Speeding up the developmental process of society	Disastrous effects on the environment (pollution, traffic, energy consumption)
Replacing human operators in tasks that involve hard physical or monotonous work	Sharp increase in **unemployment rate** due to machines replacing human beings
Saving time and money as human operators can be employed in higher-level work	Technical limitations as current technology is unable to automate all the desired tasks
Replacing human operators in **tasks** done in dangerous environments (fire, space, volcanoes, nuclear facilities, underwater)	Security threats as an automated system may have a limited level of intelligence and can make errors
Higher reliability and precision in performing tasks	Unpredictable costs due to research and development, which may exceed the cost saved by the automation itself
Economy improvement and higher productivity	High initial costs as the automation of a new product requires a large initial investment

1	manufacturing	a ☐	the time between the design of a product and its production
2	information technologies	b ☐	the amount of confidence that a group of people have
3	goods	c ☐	a set of tasks performed to complete a procedure
4	service jobs	d ☐	the process of packing and distributing goods
5	skilled	e ☐	the industry in which machinery is used to produce goods
6	morale	f ☐	the development and application of computer systems
7	unemployment	g ☐	having the knowledge and the ability to do something well
8	lead times	h ☐	things that are made to be sold
9	handling	i ☐	jobs in transports, communications, hospitals, energy industry, etc.
10	work flow	j ☐	the state of not having a job

2 Pairwork **What would you like to automate in your life? In pairs, discuss the impact of automation on your own life and list its main advantages and disadvantages.**

3 **Read the text about automation technologies and answer the questions.**

Numerical control over automated devices has resulted in a rapidly expanding range of applications and human activities. Computer-aided technologies (CAx) is a **broad** term that means the use of computer systems to **aid** in the design, analysis, and manufacture of products, by serving the basis for mathematical and organisational tools used to create complex systems. It includes computer-aided design (CAD software) and computer-aided manufacturing (CAM software).

The current limit of computer-aided technologies is that some abilities are well **beyond** the capabilities of modern mechanical and computer systems. Moreover, these technologies require high-skilled engineers and the synthesis of complex sensory data to work properly. As for costs involved, in some cases, automation is more expensive than mechanical approach.

Thanks to the incredible improvements in automation technology, a number of other technologies have developed from it, such as domotics and robotics.

Domotics is a field in building automation aimed at the application of automation technologies in households for the comfort and security of its residents. This means that lights, heating and conditioning systems, windows **shutters**, kitchen equipment and **surveillance** systems can be controlled by a remote control or even by a cell phone at a distance.

Robotics is a special branch of automation in which the automated machines have certain human features and are used to replace human workers in factory operations. Robots are computer-controlled mechanical devices that are programmed to move, manipulate objects and interact with the environment. **Nowadays** more and more sophisticated robots are being built to serve various practical purposes, for example in houses, businesses, in the **army** and for medical appliances for **disabled** people.

1 What does computer-aided technologies mean?
2 Which software does CAx include?
3 What are the current limits of CAx?
4 Can you name two applications of automation technologies?
5 How does a domotic house differ from a traditional house?
6 What are robots used for?

4 ⌂ 11 Pairwork **Think of what robots can do nowadays and tick the boxes below. Then listen and check your answers.**

Nowadays robots can...
- [ ] get sick
- [ ] **go underwater**
- [ ] handle dangerous material
- [ ] clean nuclear waste
- [ ] explore volcanoes
- [ ] go to space
- [ ] easily walk on two legs
- [ ] see obstacles
- [ ] speak fluently
- [ ] smell things
- [ ] taste food
- [ ] move objects
- [ ] have feelings

Sensors

5 Read the text about sensors and match each paragraph with a heading.

Sensor applications   Types of sensors   What is a sensor?

1 _____

Almost every industrial automated process requires the use of sensors and **transducers**, which are very advanced devices capable of measuring and sensing the environment and translating physical information (e.g. variations of light, pressure, temperature and position) into electrical signals. The sensor **picks up** the information to be measured and the transducer converts it into electrical signals that can be directly processed by the control unit of a system.

2 _____

Because of the industrial and scientific importance of measuring, sensors are widely used in a variety of fields, such as medicine, engineering, robotics, biology and manufacturing. Traditional machines have difficulty measuring small differences in product size, so sensors can be particularly useful as they can **discriminate** down to 0,00013 millimetres. They can also detect temperature, humidity and pressure, acquire data and alter the manufacturing process. Sensors are also vital components of advanced machines, such as robots.

3 _____

There are two types of sensors: analogue and digital. Analogue sensors operate with data represented by measured voltages or quantities, while digital ones have numeric or digital outputs which can be directly transmitted to computers.
The sensors usually employed in manufacturing are classified as mechanical, electrical, magnetic and thermal, but they can also be acoustic, chemical, optical and radiation sensors. Moreover, according to their method of sensing, they can be tactile or visual. Tactile sensors are sensitive to touch, force or pressure and they are used to measure and register the interaction between a contact surface and the environment. These sensors are used in innumerable everyday objects, such as **lift** buttons and lamps which turn on and off by touching the base. Visual sensors, instead, sense the presence, shape and movement of an object optically. They are becoming more and more important in surveillance systems, environment and disaster monitoring and military applications.

6 Read the text again and choose the correct answer.

1 Sensors pick up _____ to be measured.
   A electrical signals
   B physical information
   C the control unit

2 Physical data is translated into electrical signals by _____.
   A the transducer
   B the sensor
   C a computer

3 Sensors _____ used to alter the manufacturing process.
   A can't be
   B are never
   C can be

4 _____ sensors can transmit data directly to computers.
   A Chemical
   B Digital
   C Analogue

5 Tactile sensors are commonly used in _____.
   A everyday objects
   B military applications
   C sophisticated machinery

6 _____ sensors are used to localise objects in space.
   A Analogue
   B Visual
   C Tactile

7 🎧 12 **Read the text about the computer mouse and underline the correct option. Then listen and check.**

A common example of the application of sensors to everyday objects is the computer mouse.

The mechanical mouse has a ball which rotates and translates the (1) *motion/temperature* of our hand into signals that the computer can use.

Developed in late 1999, the optical mouse is an advanced computer pointing device that uses a light-emitting **diode** (LED), an (2) *acoustic/optical* sensor and a digital signal processor (DSP) in place of the traditional mouse ball and electromechanical transducer. The optical mouse actually uses a tiny (3) *camera/recorder* to take thousands of pictures at a rate of more than 1,000 images per (4) *minute/second*.

Optical mice can work on many surfaces without a mouse pad, thanks to an LED that **bounces** light **off** the surface it is on onto an optical sensor. The sensor sends each image to a digital signal (5) *processor/transistor* which examines how the **patterns** have moved since the previous image, determining how far the mouse has moved. The computer then moves the cursor on the screen based on the coordinates received from the mouse. This happens hundreds of times each second, making the cursor appear to move very (6) *slowly/smoothly*.

The best surfaces reflect but some others, for example a blank sheet of white (7) *plastic/paper*, do not allow the sensor and DSP to work properly because the details are too small to be detected.

In addition to LEDs, a recent innovation are laser-based optical mice that detect more surface details compared to LED technology. This results in the ability to use a mouse on almost any surface and to (8) *reduce/increase* the resolution of the image.

8 **Read the text again and match each sentence with its ending.**

1 A mechanical mouse	a ☐ the optical mouse was developed.
2 There are no sensors	b ☐ provide high-resolution images.
3 In late 1999	c ☐ can reflect light in the same way.
4 An optical mouse	d ☐ in a mechanical mouse.
5 A DPS	e ☐ has got a scroll ball mechanism inside.
6 Not all surfaces	f ☐ uses a light-emitting diode, an optical sensor and a DSP.
7 Laser-based optical mice	g ☐ is a processor for digital signals.

MY GLOSSARY

to aid /tu: eɪd/ _____

army /'ɑːmi/ _____

beyond /br'jɒnd/ _____

to bounce off /tə baʊnts ɒf/ _____

broad /brɔːd/ _____

diode /'daɪəʊd/ _____

disabled /dɪ'seɪbl̩d/ _____

to discriminate /tə dɪ'skrɪmɪneɪt/ _____

to go underwater /tə gəʊ ʌndə'wɔːtə(r)/ _____

goods /gʊds/ _____

handling /'hændlɪŋ/ _____

lead times /'liːd taɪms/ _____

lift /lɪft/ _____

manufacturing /mænjʊ'fæktʃərɪŋ/ _____

nowadays /'naʊədeɪz/ _____

pattern /'pætn/ _____

to pick up /tə 'pɪk ʌp/ _____

requirement /rɪ'kwaɪəmənt/ _____

shutter /'ʃʌtə(r)/ _____

surveillance /sə'veɪlənts/ _____

task /tɑːsk/ _____

transducer /trænz'djuːsə(r)/ _____

unemployment rate /ʌnɪm'plɔɪment reɪt/ _____

work flow /wɜːk fləʊ/ _____

Drive train

The drive train is the system that makes a car move. It includes the engine, which burns fuel to produce the mechanical energy that moves the car, as well as the **transmission**, which changes the gear differential to use the power produced by the engine efficiently. It can also include the fuel system, which consists of the tank, various filters, fuel injectors or carburettors, the exhaust system which removes the engine's waste products, the coolant system which prevents the engine from overheating, and the braking system which stops the car. Transmissions are either automatic or manual. Manual transmission involves a device, controlled by the driver, that transmits power to the wheels and it features mechanical gear sets that are engaged by the gear lever operated by the driver. Automatic transmission, on the other hand, requires no direct driver input once put into drive and leaves the operator free to focus on driving. Automatic transmission is now electronically controlled and integrated into the vehicle's powertrain control system, which means the computer in the car decides when and what gear to shift into. The primary job of any transmission is to match engine speed to vehicle speed. Internal combustion engines produce useable power over a specific range of engine speed or rpm (revolutions per minute). The transmission is utilised to keep the engine in that sweet spot or rpm through the vehicle's range of speeds.

1 Read the text and answer the questions.

1 What is the main function of the drive train system?
2 What does a drive train system include?
3 What is the function of the engine?
4 What is the main function of the transmission once power is transmitted from the engine to the axle?
5 What are the main differences between manual and automatic transmissions?
6 What are the most important components of the chassis?

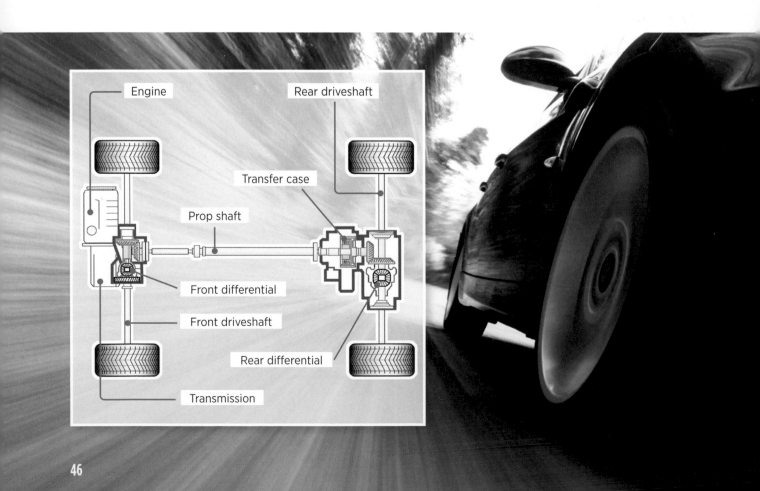

Engine
Rear driveshaft
Transfer case
Prop shaft
Front differential
Front driveshaft
Rear differential
Transmission

2 Translate these terms into your own language.

1 fuel system _____
2 tank _____
3 fuel injector _____

4 exhaust system _____
5 gear _____
6 gear lever _____

3 🎧 13 **Listen to a mechanic talking about the differential and fill in the gaps to complete the passage.**

A differential is installed to allow a (**1**) _____ difference between the inboard
and the outboard drive (**2**) _____. The components of a differential are a pinion
(**3**) _____ driven by the transmission and the (**4**) _____,
a ring gear driven by the pinion gear, and a set of spider gear driven by the ring gear.
The action of the (**5**) _____ gears allows one wheel to spin faster or slower
than the other as long as the average of the two speeds is the same as the speed of the
(**6**) _____ gear.
The differential has three tasks:
• to aim the engine (**7**) _____ at the wheels;
• to act as the final gear reduction in the vehicle, slowing the rotational speed of the
  (**8**) _____ final time before it hits the wheels;
• to transmit the power to the wheels while allowing them to (**9**) _____ at
  different speeds. This is the one that earned the (**10**) _____ its name.

The four-stroke engine

Almost all cars currently use what is called a four-stroke combustion cycle (also known as the **Otto cycle**, from the name of its inventor Nikolaus Otto in 1876) to convert petrol into motion. The driving force behind the movement of a car is a device called an internal **combustion** engine. Within this engine, there is a constant cycle of ignition and combustion. Fuel is ignited by spark plugs, and it burns the air available to create an explosion. This cycle provides mechanical energy, which provides the power for the car. The main parts of the engine all work together to facilitate this process. The four strokes are:

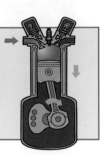

Fuel/air intake As the piston makes its way towards the high point of its motion, a mixture of fuel and air is injected into the cylinder through a carburettor or a fuel injection system. A proper mix of fuel with air enables the piston to function optimally.

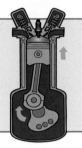

Compression As the piston nears the top of its up-and-down motion, it compresses the fuel and air that has been injected into the cylinder. Compression increases the explosiveness of a combustible material.

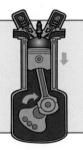

Combustion/power At the moment that the piston hits the top of the cylinder, the fuel is ignited by a spark from a spark plug. The resulting combustion pushes the piston back down to the bottom of the cylinder.

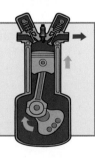

Exhaust Just as the heat and smoke from a fireplace fire has to be expelled through a chimney, the same is true of the combustion in an engine cylinder. When a car's piston is propelled downward, the residue of the combustion is expelled through an exhaust valve in the cylinder wall and goes out through the exhaust pipe.

Now the engine is ready for the next cycle, so it intakes another charge of air and gas. In an engine the linear movement of the pistons is converted into rotational motion by the crankshaft. The rotational motion makes the car's wheels move.

The area where compression and combustion take place is called the combustion chamber. The difference between the maximum and minimum volume of the combustion chamber is called displacement.

4 Read the text and rearrange the following sentences in the correct order 1-4.

a ☐ As the piston returns to the top of its stroke, the intake valve closes and the mixture of air and fuel is compressed.

b ☐ When a car piston is propelled downward, the residue of the combustion is expelled through an exhaust valve in the cylinder wall and goes out through the exhaust pipe.

c ☐ A spark from a spark plug ignites the compressed gas. The resulting combustion pushes the piston back down to the bottom of the cylinder.

d ☐ The piston starts at the top, the intake valve opens, and the piston moves down to let the engine take in air and fuel.

5 Match the words with their definitions.

1 valve
2 combustion
3 ignition
4 piston

a ☐ the process of burning
b ☐ the electrical part of a vehicle's engine that makes it start working
c ☐ the part of an engine that moves up and down
d ☐ part of a tube or pipe that opens and shuts to control the flow of liquid, gas, air, etc. passing through it

6 Pairwork Look at the picture and translate the terms into your own language.

1 intake valve ___
2 connecting rod ___
3 clutch ___
4 flywheel ___
5 piston ___
6 exhaust cam ___
7 gearbox ___
8 exhaust valve ___
9 intake cam ___
10 crank (shaft) ___
11 spark plug ___

Spark plug
Intake cam
Exhaust cam
Exhaust valve
Intake valve
Clutch
Piston
Gearbox
Connecting rod
Flywheel
Crank

7 🎧 14 Listen to a description of the ignition process and then fill in the gaps with the missing words.

When the car key turns the engine on, the (1) ___ from the battery travels to the starter and distributor. The (2) ___ in the engine uses electric battery (3) ___ to begin rotating the engine's (4) ___ . The electric battery power traveling to the distributor is distributed to all the spark (5) ___ in the engine block. Once the starter begins to rotate the crankshaft, the (6) ___ in the engine block begin to stroke up and down. When the piston goes down, a (7) ___ injector mists a gas-and-oxygen mixture into the piston chamber. As the piston begins to travel back up, it compresses the gas and oxygen mix. At the top of the (8) ___ , the spark plug fires, and the small (9) ___ fires the piston back down and starts the crankshafts (10) ___ in a rotating motion.

8 Speaking Prepare a short presentation (2-5 minutes) of the following topics and then report to your classmates.

• the combustion cycle   • the four strokes   • the ignition

The two-stroke engine

A two-stroke engine uses a mixture of fuel and oil as fuel. On the upstroke, the piston compresses the air/fuel mix in the combustion chamber. At the same time it pulls a fresh air/fuel mix into the crankcase for the next cycle. When the ignition sparks, it burns the mix forcing the piston downwards, opening the exhaust port while simultaneously forcing the air/fuel mix that was in the crankcase into the combustion chamber, as well as the spent exhaust out through the exhaust port. At this point it repeats the process.

That is why fuel and oil are mixed together. The oil in the mix lubricates the motor.

One of the main parts of a two-stroke engine is a crankcase that surrounds and protects all other parts of the engine. Inside, it has a crankshaft, connecting rod and single piston. It has also got an intake port, a reed valve, an exhaust port, and a cylinder–all in addition to the combustion chamber where the power is produced that moves whatever the engine is powering.

The crankshaft in a two-stroke engine rotates, moving the piston by means of the connecting rod. These three parts are the only moving parts in a two-stroke engine. All power produced is a direct result of the action of these three moving parts. The connecting rod is connected to the crankshaft at one end, and to the piston at the other. It translates the movement of the crankshaft so that the piston is moved up and down.

A two-stroke engine is commonly found in lower-power applications. Some of the devices that might have a two-stroke engine include garden equipment (lawn mowers, chainsaws, trimmers), dirt bikes, mopeds, jet skis, small outboard motors. The lower cost to rebuild and maintain made the two-stroke engine incredibly popular. Most small designs use petrol lubrication, with the oil being burned in the combustion chamber, causing 'blue smoke' and other types of exhaust pollution. This is a major reason why two-stroke engines were replaced by four-stroke engines in many applications.

9 **Read the text and decide if the statements below are true (T) or false (F).**

1 A two-stroke engine is commonly found in higher power applications.
2 The first commercial two-stroke engine involving in-cylinder compression is attributed to Joseph Day.
3 One of the main reasons for the two-stroke engines loss of popularity was the fact that it caused blue smoke and other kinds of pollution.
4 On the upstroke, the piston compresses the air/fuel mix in the combustion chamber.
5 When the ignition sparks, it burns the mix forcing the piston up.
6 Inside the crankcase there is a crankshaft, connecting rod and single piston and other components.

10 Read the text and rearrange the following sentences in the correct order 1-9.

a ☐ When the piston reaches the top,

b ☐ New fuel and air travel via the intake port into the cylinder, ready to be burnt.

c ☐ the spark plug then lights the air/fuel mixture, burning it and sending the piston back down.

d ☐ The piston is moved up and down inside the cylinder by the crankshaft, which is connected to it via the connecting rod.

e ☐ The exhaust is expelled through the exhaust port,

f ☐ A vacuum is formed as it takes its upward stroke, drawing air and fuel down through the reed valve.

g ☐ and an unpleasant side effect is that it usually takes some of the unburned fuel mixture with it.

h ☐ On the downward stroke,

i ☐ the reed valve gets closed because of the increased pressure of the fuel and air mixture within, which is being compressed.

11 Match the words with their definitions.

1 fuel	a ☐	the process of maintaining a fluid film between solid parts
2 pump	b ☐	a machine or tool that does a special job
3 device	c ☐	a substance such as oil or gas that can be burned to produce heat or energy
4 lubrication	d ☐	a long piece of metal in a vehicle that is connected to the engine and helps to urn the wheels
5 rod		
6 crankshaft	e ☐	a machine for forcing liquid or gas into or out of something
7 pollution	f ☐	a long thin pole or stick
	g ☐	the process of making water, air, or land dangerous especially with poisonous chemicals

12 **Writing** Look at the picture of a two-stroke engine. What are the main differences in terms of components from the four-stroke one? Write a short paragraph.

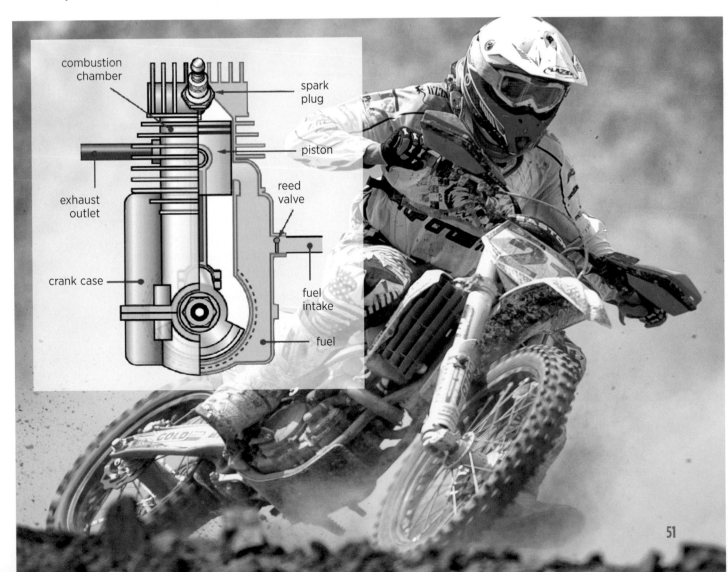

The diesel engine

In 1893 German inventor and mechanical engineer Rudolf Diesel invented the engine which still carries his name. The basic difference between a diesel engine or **compression-ignition engine** and a petrol engine is that a petrol engine needs an ignition system that uses an electric spark to be started. Diesel engines do not. In a diesel engine, the fuel is sprayed into the combustion chambers through fuel injector nozzles just when the air in each chamber has been placed under such great pressure that it is hot enough to ignite the fuel spontaneously. This is what happens when a diesel-powered vehicle is started. When the key in the ignition is turned a process begins in which fuel is injected into the cylinders under such high pressure that it heats the air in the cylinders all by itself.

The time it takes to warm things up has been dramatically reduced – probably no more than 1.5 seconds in moderate weather.

Diesel fuel is less volatile than petrol and it is easier to start if the combustion chamber is preheated, so manufacturers originally installed little glow plugs that worked off the battery to pre-warm the air in the cylinders when the engine was started. Better fuel management techniques and higher injection pressures now create enough heat to touch off the fuel without glow plugs, but the plugs are still in there for emissions control as the extra heat they provide helps burn the fuel more efficiently. Some vehicles still have these chambers whereas others do not, but the results are still the same. When there is pressure on the accelerator and the ignition key is turned to Start the fuel passes through a couple of fuel filters that clean it before it can get to the fuel injector nozzles. Proper filter maintenance is especially important in diesels because fuel contamination can clog up the tiny holes in the injector nozzles. A delivery tube keeps it under constant high pressure while it delivers the fuel to each cylinder at the proper time.

Diesel engines are used in heavy equipment, locomotives, ships and vehicles.

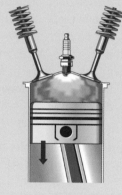

Gas engine

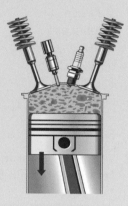

Diesel engine

13 **Read the text and choose the correct option.**

1 A diesel engine
 A is very similar in build to a petrol engine.
 B is completely different in build to a petrol engine.
 C has more differences than similarities to a petrol engine.

2 The main difference between a diesel and a petrol engine is that
 A the diesel engine has spark plugs to ignite the fuel.
 B the diesel engine has no spark plugs to ignite the fuel.
 C the diesel engine has a mixed system to ignite the fuel.

3 In a diesel engine fuel is sprayed into the combustion chamber
 A at the end of the compression stroke.
 B before the compression stroke.
 C during the compression stroke.

4 Diesel fuel is
 A less volatile than petrol.
 B as volatile as petrol.
 C more volatile than petrol.

5 Filter maintenance in diesels is
 A as important as in petrol.
 B irrelevant.
 C more important than in petrol.

14 **Read the text again and match the two parts of the sentences.**

1 Turning the key begins a process
2 The pressure of the fuel injection
3 The fuel passes through a couple of
4 Fuel contamination

a ☐ filters that clean it before it can get to the fuel injector nozzle.
b ☐ can clog up the holes in the injector nozzles.
c ☐ in which fuel is injected into the filters cylinders.
d ☐ is so high that it heats the air in the cylinders all by itself.

15 Translate these terms into your own language.

1 combustion chamber _____
2 manufacturers _____
3 injection pressure _____
4 emission control _____

5 filter maintenance _____
6 fuel contamination _____
7 high pressure _____
8 heavy equipment _____

16 Complete the text about biodiesel with the words from the box.

> engine   exhaust   fuel   to run   oil   peanut

A diesel (**1**) _____ can also run on
vegetable (**2**) _____ made from old
cooking oil. This type of (**3**) _____ is
called biodiesel. Running a diesel engine on biodiesel
fuel makes the (**4**) _____ fumes smell
like food. Using vegetable oil (**5**) _____
an engine is not a new idea. Incredible enough, the
engine that Rudolf Diesel used to demonstrate his new
idea ran on (**6**) _____ _____ oil.

17 Speaking Prepare a short presentation about how a diesel engine works with the help of the guidelines below.

• What are the main differences between a petrol and a diesel engine?
• Why does the fuel burn immediately?
• Where are diesel engines used?

MY GLOSSARY

carburettor /kɑːbjʊˈrɛtə/ _____
crankcase /ˈkraŋkkeɪs/ _____
crankshaft /ˈkraŋkʃɑːft/ _____
cylinder /ˈsɪlɪndə/ _____
differential /dɪfəˈrɛnʃ(ə)l/ _____
four-stroke /fɔː strəʊk/ _____
gear lever /ɡɪəˈliːvə/ _____
ignition /ɪɡˈnɪʃ(ə)n/ _____
inboard /ˈɪnbɔːd/ _____

intake /ˈɪnteɪk/ _____
nozzle /ˈnɒz(ə)l/ _____
outboard /ˈaʊtbɔːd/ _____
powertrain /ˈpaʊətreɪn/ _____
spark /spɑːk/ _____
sweet spot /swiːt spɒt/ _____
transmission /trɑːnsˈmɪʃ(ə)n/ _____
two-stroke /tuːstrəʊk/ _____
valve /valv/ _____

14 Technical assistance

1 **Read the text about maintenance and answer the questions.**

Any machine and device must be controlled regularly in order to avoid the risk of damage or breakdown of single parts **due to** long usage. Sometimes, if a proper maintenance is not done, a fault could occur, with negative consequences on the production process and on the workers' safety. The primary goal of maintenance is to avoid or mitigate the consequences of **failure** of equipment. This includes performing routine actions to keep the device in working order and prevent the failure before it actually occurs (preventive maintenance), or fixing equipment after breakdown (corrective maintenance).

Preventive maintenance is designed to preserve and restore equipment reliability by replacing **worn** components before they actually fail. It includes maintenance activities such as partial or complete **overhauls** at specified periods, oil changes and **lubrication**. The ideal preventive maintenance is a combination of technical, administrative and managerial actions to prevent all equipment failure. If carried out properly, preventive maintenance can extend the life of the equipment.

Corrective maintenance, sometimes simply called 'repair', is carried out to get equipment working again. It **aims at** restoring the functionality of a machine so that it can continue to perform its work. This type of maintenance can be very expensive because sometimes equipment needs to be replaced, with substantial costs for the company.

Generally, maintenance is **scheduled** according to:
- the original equipment manufacturer's recommendations;
- codes and legislation within a country;
- **consultancy** advice;
- previous maintenance;
- most important measured values and performance indications.

1 Why is maintenance important?
2 What are the main types of maintenance?
3 What is the function of preventive maintenance?
4 Which activities does it include?
5 What is maintenance called if it occurs after a failure?
6 Why can corrective maintenance be expensive?

2 **Read the text again and match the words with their definitions.**

1	fault	a ☐	damaged and in poor condition as a result of much use
2	to mitigate	b ☐	a set of rules about how something must be done
3	to fix	c ☐	expert advice within a particular field
4	overhaul	d ☐	applying a greasy substance to reduce friction
5	worn	e ☐	a break or other defect in a piece of machinery
6	lubrication	f ☐	to do the necessary work to repair something that doesn't work properly
7	code	g ☐	to make something less severe or unpleasant
8	consultancy	h ☐	a careful examination of a machinery or system that must be repaired

Auto maintenance

3 How well do you know the components of a car? Look at the picture and label each part with the words in the box.

| seat | battery | radiator | **tyre** | spare wheel | steering wheel |
| disk **brake** | oil filter | **trunk** | windshield wiper |

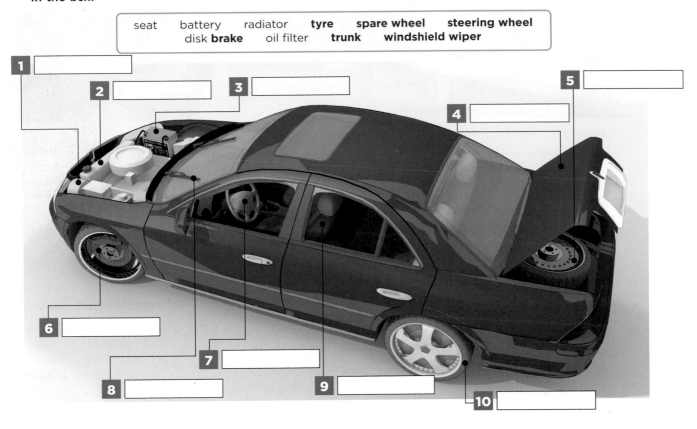

1

2

3

5

4

6

7

8

9

10

4 Quiz In pairs, take this quiz about car maintenance, then read the text to check your answers.

Cars are not just a luxury item to purchase one day and forget about until something happens. A properly maintained car not only lasts longer, but it is also less likely to break down unexpectedly. Take this quiz and test your knowledge of car maintenance!

1 Auto maintenance doesn't **entail** replacing fluids.
True ☐ False ☐

2 It is not possible to do preventive maintenance to cars.
True ☐ False ☐

3 Car maintenance must be scheduled keeping in mind different factors.
True ☐ False ☐

4 The distance travelled every day doesn't affect the functionality of a car.
True ☐ False ☐

5 If a car is exposed to extreme weather conditions it must be checked more often.
True ☐ False ☐

6 It is not possible to replace windshield wipers.
True ☐ False ☐

7 Brake fluid lasts forever.
True ☐ False ☐

8 Car maintenance tasks should never be combined in one single service.
True ☐ False ☐

5 Read the text and match the correct maintenance task with each picture.

Auto maintenance describes the act of inspecting or testing the condition of car subsystems (e.g.: **engine**, brakes, radiator, etc.) and replacing parts and fluids. Thanks to regular maintenance it is possible to ensure the safety, reliability and comfort of a car, while during preventive maintenance, a number of parts are replaced to avoid major damage or for safety reasons.

Car maintenance is usually scheduled according to different factors, such as the year or model of the car, its driving condition and driver **behaviour**. When scheduling auto maintenance, car manufacturers recommend keeping in mind some factors that may affect the functionality of car subsystems. Some of these factors are: the number of trips and the distance travelled every day; the **exposure** to particular climate conditions (extreme hot or cold); long-distance cruising and whether the car has to **tow** a **trailer** or other heavy loads.

Common car maintenance tasks include:

- car wash
- check or replace the engine oil and oil filters
- inspect or replace windshield wipers
- inspect tyre pressure and **wear**
- check wheel **alignment**
- check, clean or replace battery terminals
- inspect or replace **brake pads** and fluids
- inspect or replace air filter
- lubricate **locks** and **hinges**
- check all lights
- inspect or replace **spark plugs**
- **tighten chassis bolts**

Some tasks that have equivalent service intervals can be combined into one single service known as a tune-up. In modern cars, where electronics control most of the car's functions, the traditional tune-up has been replaced by incorporated software that takes care of the engine by constantly checking thousands of sensor signals. Completed maintenance services are then recorded in a **service book** which is very useful for keeping track of the car service history.

6 🎧 15 **Listen to the dialogue between Mrs Farrell and her mechanic and complete it with the missing words.**

Mechanic	Good afternoon, Mrs Farrell.
Mrs Farrell	Good afternoon, John. How are you?
Mechanic	I'm fine, thank you. How can I (1) *help* you?
Mrs Farrell	Well, I need a complete (2) _____ for my car. Next week my husband and I are going on holiday by car. It's going to be a long journey all the way to Spain and I want my car to be in (3) _____.
Machanic	Sure. No problem. Have you checked your car recently?
Mrs Farrell	Let me think... It must have been last year, in June, when the car wouldn't (4) _____. Anyway, it should all be written in the (5) _____. It's in the **glove compartment**.
Mechanic	OK, I'll take it. Let's see... Oh, yes, it was the battery and I changed it. Are there any problems at the moment?
Mrs Farrell	Not really, but I think the (6) _____ needs to be replaced.
Mechanic	Sure. I'll check the filters too.
Mrs Farrell	Yes, I think it's a good idea. Could you (7) _____ the tyres as well? And maybe wash it; it's so dirty. Well, John, when do you think the car will be ready?
Mechanic	Actually, I'm quite busy at the moment, Mrs Farrell, so I could give it back to you next Friday. Would that be convenient for you?
Mrs Farrell	Yes, it'd be perfect, because we're leaving on Sunday. I'll call you on Tuesday for a confirmation then.
Mechanic	All right. Goodbye, Mrs Farrell.
on Friday...	
Mechanic	Good morning, Mrs Farrell. Here are your keys. I replaced the engine oil and the (8) _____. Then I checked the tyres and the brakes too. I had to (9) _____ the spark plugs because they were **fouled**. I also (10) _____ the electronics and then I washed the car. Now everything is OK, you can **set off** with no worries.
Mrs Farrell	That's great! Thank you very much, John.

7 **Read the dialogue again and answer the questions.**

1 What does Mrs Farrell want?
2 Why does she need a complete tune-up?
3 What is written in the service book?
4 What does the car need to be done?
5 When will the car be ready?
6 What did John replace in the car?

MY GLOSSARY

to aim at /tuː eɪm ət/ _____
alignment /əˈlaɪnmənt/ _____
behaviour /bɪˈheɪvjə(r)/ _____
bolt /bəʊlt/ _____
brake /breɪk/ _____
brake pad /breɪk pæd/ _____
chassis /ˈʃæsi/ _____
consultancy /kənˈsʌltənsi/ _____
due to /djuː tə/ _____
to entail /tuː ɪnˈteɪl/ _____
exposure /ɪkˈspəʊʒə(r)/ _____
failure /ˈfeɪljə(r)/ _____
fouled /faʊld/ _____
glove compartment /glʌv kəmˈpɑːtmənt/ _____
hinge /hɪndʒ/ _____
lock /lɒk/ _____

lubrication /luːbrɪˈkeɪʃn _____
overhaul /ˈəʊvəhɔːl/ _____
to schedule /tə ˈʃedjuːl/ _____
service book /sɜːvɪs bʊk/ _____
to set off /tə set ɒf/ _____
spare wheel /speə(r) wiːl/ _____
spark plug /spɑːk plʌg/ _____
steering wheel /stɪərɪŋ wiːl/ _____
to tighten /tə ˈtaɪtn/ _____
to tow /tə təʊ/ _____
trailer /treɪlə(r)/ _____
trunk /trʌŋk/ _____
tyre /taɪə(r)/ _____
wear /weə(r)/ _____
windshield /wɪndʃiːld/ _____
worn /wɔːn/ _____

15 Health and safety at work

1 Read the text about health and safety at work and answer the questions.

Attention must be paid to **safety** in order to ensure a safe working practice in factories. Workers must be aware of the dangers and risks that exist all around them: two out of every three industrial accidents are caused by individual **carelessness**. In order to avoid or reduce accidents, both protective and **precautionary** measures must be followed while working.

Each country has specific regulations concerning health and safety at work. For example, The Health and Safety at Work Act 1974 is a UK Act of Parliament that establishes the fundamental rules to enforce workplace health, safety and welfare within the United Kingdom.

The objectives of the Act are:

- to secure the health, safety and welfare of people at work;
- to protect people in the work place against risks to health or safety in connection to their work activities;
- to control the keeping and use of dangerous substances;
- to control the emission of dangerous gases into the atmosphere.

The Act defines general duties of **employers**, **employees**, **suppliers** of goods and substances for use at work, and people who manage and maintain work premises. In particular, every employer has to ensure the health, safety and welfare at work of all the employees, visitors, the general public and clients. Employers have to ensure the absence of risk to health in connection with the use, handling or storage of items and substances, as well as provide adequate facilities for a safe working environment. It is also very important to provide employees with proper instructions and training so that they will be able **to cope with** any problem that may occur at work.

Employees, on their part, should always behave responsibly at work and take care of themselves and other people who may be affected by their actions. Moreover, they should cooperate with employers to **enable** them to perform their duties or requirements under the Act.

1 Why is it important to ensure a safe working environment?
2 Which law regulates workers' welfare in the United Kingdom?
3 What does the Act define?
4 What are the duties of employers?
5 Why is it important to provide employees with adequate training?
6 How can employees contribute to a safe working environment?

2 Read the text again and match the words with their definitions.

1	precautionary measure	a ☐	a responsibility or task that you have to do as part of your job
2	carelessness	b ☐	to deal effectively with a difficult situation
3	welfare	c ☐	the buildings and land occupied by a business
4	duty	d ☐	poor attention to an activity, which results in harm or errors
5	premises	e ☐	action taken in order to prevent something dangerous from happening
6	to cope with	f ☐	the health, comfort and well-being of a person or group

3 🎧 16 **This is an example of safety rules established by the workers' safety committee in a factory in Adelaide, Australia. Read the text and complete it with the words in the box, then listen and check.**

operate   tidy   **fire**   gloves   concentration   first aid   protection   brush

SAFETY RULES

MACHINERY ▐▐▐▐▐▐▐▐▐▐▐▐▐▐

■ Be sure to understand how to (1) *operate* every machine you are going to use.
■ Never use machinery when you are in a room alone.
■ Use all the (2) _____ required in the place of work.
■ Check that the safety devices are working. If they are not working, ask for them to be repaired immediately.
■ Do not talk to anybody who is operating a machine. (3) _____ is important at all times.
■ Turn off the electricity before cleaning a machine.

TOOLS ▐▐▐▐▐▐▐▐▐▐▐▐▐▐▐

■ Report any damage to the tools used at work.
■ See that tools are correctly set.

DRESS ▐▐▐▐▐▐▐▐▐▐▐▐▐▐▐▐

■ Before starting work, wear protective clothing.
■ Always wear safety glasses, (4) _____ and boots when using a machine.

WORKSHOP ▐▐▐▐▐▐▐▐▐▐▐▐▐

■ Keep the workshop (5) _____, do not leave rubbish around and do not throw cigarette ends or **ashes** into the rubbish bin.
■ The area around machines must be kept clear to avoid falling.
■ Tools and protective clothing should be put away when not in use.
■ Clean machines after use with a (6) _____ not with your hands.

ACCIDENT PROCEDURES ▐▐▐▐▐▐▐▐▐

■ Make sure you know where to **assemble** in the event of (7) _____ and where the emergency stop buttons are located.
■ Check where the **fire extinguishers** are in your workplace and how they work, in order to be able to use them in case of fire.
■ Do not shout or run as this can lead to panic, and inform the supervisor immediately if any accident occurs.
■ Never administer (8) _____ unless you have been trained to do so.

4 **Read the text again and decide if the following rules are true (T) or false (F), then correct the false ones.**

1 Use machinery only when other people are in the workplace. _____
2 People mustn't talk in the workplace. _____
3 Turn off electricity after a machine has been cleaned. _____
4 Wear safety boots before arriving in a workplace. _____
5 Always wear sunglasses when using a machine. _____
6 Damaged tools can be dangerous. _____
7 Report to the supervisor about damaged equipment. _____
8 In case of fire ask the supervisor where the emergency stop buttons are located. _____
9 In case of fire shout to catch other people's attention. _____
10 Anyone can give first aid in case of an accident. _____

5 Read the text about safety signs and colours and complete the table with the correct sign category.

Safety **signs** and colours are useful tools to help protect the health and safety of employees and workplace visitors. Safety signs are used to draw attention to health and safety **hazards**, to point out hazards which may not be obvious and to remind employees where personal protective equipment must be worn.

Colour attracts attention and can be used extensively for safety purposes. For example, colour can be used as an additional safety measure to identify the contents of pipes and the nature of the hazard.

Different combinations of colours are used to indicate the various types of hazards. For example, the colour red is used to indicate a definite hazard, while a potential hazard is communicated by the colour yellow.

When employees are aware of the hazards around them and take the necessary precautions, the possibility of an **injury**, illness or other loss is minimised.

As shown in the table below, there are three basic sign categories used in the workplace:
* warning, to indicate definite or potential hazards;
* regulatory, to indicate which actions are prohibited or mandatory;
* information, to provide general information and directions.

Each category is distinguished by its shape and can be divided into subcategories having different colours.

Category	Subcategory	Colour
1 _____ A circle indicates that an order is in force.	- Prohibition: it forbids an action. - Mandatory: it requires an action.	Red and black on white White on black
2 _____ A triangle indicates caution or danger.	- Caution: it indicates a potential hazard. - Danger: it indicates a definite hazard.	Black on yellow White on red
3 _____ A square indicates information.	- Emergency: it indicates first aid, health, fire protection and emergency equipment. - General information: it indicates permission or public information.	White on green White on blue

6 Match each sign with its meaning and write the correct subcategory for each of them.

a ☐ slippery when wet
b ☐ high voltage
c ☐ first aid station
d ☐ head protection must be worn
e ☐ cafeteria
f ☐ no smoking area

7 Read the texts about safety equipment and match the words in the box with the correct description.

> hearing protection   hard hats   respirator   safety glasses   face shield   **overall**

(1) _____ are the most important piece of safety equipment. There are many styles of these, but all share the same features, that is to say impact resistant **lenses** and side screens to protect against dust.

(2) _____ should be worn when working with **loud** power tools and machinery, in order to protect you from long-term hearing loss.

(3) _____ are predominantly used in workplace environments such as **building sites**. They protect the head from injury by falling objects, impact with other objects, **debris**, bad weather and electric shock.

When working with chemicals or machinery which makes dust, it is advisable to wear a face mask, to keep these fine particles away from the face. When spraying **varnish** or paint, a (4) _____ is a better choice, to protect you from any **harmful** effects of using these **chemicals**.

(5) A _____ must be worn when using machinery which gives off **sparks** or little parts. It is comfortable, can be **flipped up** when not needed, and will keep most of the flying chips away from your face.

When working, you should always wear proper clothing, like an (6) _____.
Comfortable, **long-sleeved** shirts and long trousers combined with good safety boots will each provide a layer of protection.

8 🎧 17 Listen to the dialogues and complete the table with the equipment and the hazard mentioned.

Dialogue	Equipment	Hazard
1		
2		
3		
4		

9 Read the text about fire safety procedures and put the actions in the correct order.

A fire safety plan is required in all public buildings, from schools, hospitals, supermarkets to workplaces. Generally, the owner of the building is responsible for the preparation of a fire safety plan. Once the plan has been approved by the Chief Fire Official, the owner is responsible for training all staff in their duties.

Evacuation drills are a very important part of the staff training associated with emergency evacuation procedures. Drills should be carried out in all buildings at least once a year. The drill should be checked, recording the time required to complete the evacuation, and noting any problems and deficiencies. After each drill a meeting should be held to evaluate the success of the drill and to solve any problems that may have arisen.

What to do in case of fire…

- If you see fire or smoke, do not panic. Remain calm and move quickly, but do not run.
- Alert the responsible staff and telephone the correct national emergency number. Have someone meet the **firefighters** to tell them where the fire is. They can lose valuable minutes if they have to find it themselves.
- Rescue any people in immediate danger only if it is safe to do so.
- If practicable, close all doors and windows to contain the fire.
- Try to extinguish the fire using appropriate firefighting equipment only if you are trained and it is safe to do so.
- Follow the instructions of your supervisor and prepare to evacuate if necessary.
- Save **records** if possible.
- Evacuate your area and check all rooms, especially changing rooms, toilets, storage areas, etc.
- Do a head count of all staff and report any people unaccounted for to the supervisor.

a ☐ Close all doors and windows.
b ☐ Do a head count of all staff and visitors.
c ☐ Evacuate your area and check all rooms.
d ☐ Meet the firefighters and give them details about the fire.
e ☐ Save records.
f ☐ Prepare to evacuate.
g ☐ *1* Remain calm and move quickly.
h ☐ Report any people unaccounted for to the supervisor.
i ☐ Rescue any people in immediate danger.
j ☐ Telephone the correct national emergency number.
k ☐ Try to extinguish the fire using appropriate firefighting equipment.

MY GLOSSARY

ash /æʃ/ _____
to assemble /tuː əˈsembl̩/ _____
building site /ˈbɪldɪŋ saɪt/ _____
carelessness /ˈkeərləsnəs/ _____
chemicals /ˈkemɪkls/ _____
to cope with /tə kəʊp wɪð/ _____
debris /ˈdebriː/ _____
employee /ɪmˈplɔɪiː/ _____
employer /ɪmˈplɔɪə(r)/ _____
to enable /tuː ɪˈneɪbl̩/ _____
evacuation drill /ɪvækjuˈeɪʃn drɪl/ _____
fire extinguisher /faɪə(r) ɪkˈstɪŋgwɪʃə(r)/ _____
fire fighter /faɪə(r) faɪtə(r)/ _____
to flip up /tə flɪp ʌp/ _____

harmful /ˈhɑːmfəl/ _____
hazard /ˈhæzəd/ _____
injury /ˈɪndʒri/ _____
lens /lenz/ _____
long-sleeved /lɒŋsliːvd/ _____
loud /laʊd/ _____
overall /əʊvərˈɔːl/ _____
precautionary /prɪˈkɔːʃnəri/ _____
record /ˈrekɔːd/ _____
safety /ˈseɪfti/ _____
sign /saɪn/ _____
spark /spɑːk/ _____
supplier /səˈplaɪə(r)/ _____
varnish /ˈvɑːnɪʃ/ _____

Symbols

Symbol	Example	Meaning in full
.	3.14	three point one four
+	a + b	a plus b
-	c - d	c minus d
=	T = 24	T equals twenty four
x	3 x 10	three multiplied by ten / three times ten
:	16:8	sixteen divided by eight
%	10%	ten per cent
°	20°	twenty degrees
>	> 10	greater than ten
<	< 20	less than twenty
≤	≤12	less than or equal to twelve
≥	≥30	greater than or equal to thirty
√	√16	the square root of sixteen
$n^{2, 3, 4...}$	10^3	ten to the power of three
{}		curly brackets
[]		square brackets
()		round brackets
∞	A ∞ B	A is proportional to B

Electrical units

Name	Measurement of	Symbol
Volt	Electrical pressure	V
Ampere	Flow of electrons	A
Watt	Power	W
Ohm	Resistance of current flow	Ω
Hertz	Frequency	Hz

Conventional metric units

Name	Multiplication	Symbol
nano	10^{-9}	n
micro	10^{-6}	μ
milli	10^{-3}	m
kilo	10^3	k
mega	10^6	M
giga	10^9	G
tera	10^{12}	T

Flash on English for MECHANICS & ELECTRONICS
Second Edition

Editorial coordination and project: Simona Franzoni
Editorial department: Sabina Cedraro, Serena Polverino
Art director: Marco Mercatali
Page design: Sergio Elisei
Picture research: Giorgia D'Angelo
Production manager: Francesco Capitano
Page layout: Sara Blasigh, Federico Borsella
Illustrated by Laura Bresciani

Cover
Cover design: Paola Lorenzetti
Photo: Shutterstock

© 2016 ELI S.r.l
P.O. Box 6
62019 Recanati
Italy
Tel. +39 071 750701
Fax. +39 071 977851
info@elionline.com
www.elionline.com

The publisher would like to thank Rebecca Raynes for her precious contribution.

Printed by Tecnostampa - Pigini Group Printing Division - Loreto, Trevi - Italy
16.83.209.0

ISBN 978-88-536-2180-1

Photo acknowledgement
ELI archive, Shutterstock